Beating the Bends

*The Diver's Guide to Avoiding
Decompression Sickness*

By Alex Brylske

Beating the Bends

The Diver's Guide to Avoiding Decompression Sickness

by Alex Brylske

Editors: Deborah Street and Susan Holly
Photography: Steve Fish, Lynn Laymon, Lynn Seldon Jr.,
  Steve Barnett, and Divers Alert Network
Cover design: Wes Flynn
Additional art: Ron Symes, Eileen Akers

Copyright © 1995 Instructional Technologies, Inc.

Dive Training
1200 South Federal Highway, Suite 301
Boynton Beach, FL 33435

ISBN 0-9639960-4-5

Table of Contents

To Deb—my unappreciated editor, wife, and best friend—who gives clarity and meaning not only to my obtuse writing, but to my life as well. And to the men of the Edgemere Volunteer Water Rescue Unit—particularly Lou Masucci, Larry O'Leary, and Dick Robb—for your guidance and inspiration so many years ago.

Acknowledgments

A book like *Beating the Bends* would be impossible without the unselfish assistance of a lot of people. I would especially like to thank Dr. Dudley Crosson, my technical advisor and friend, for his guidance throughout this project and for his review of the manuscript. An equal share of thanks also goes to Dr. Raymond E. Rogers, who not only spent hours meticulously reviewing the manuscript, but was the inspiration for my interest in this subject. A special thanks as well to senior scientist Ron Nishi of the Canadian Defence and Civil Institute for Environmental Medicine and Gain Wong of Universal Dive Techtronics for their extensive input on DCIEM research and decompression models.

While it's the content of a book that's the final measure of its worth, credit must also go to those who have the foresight and tenacity to bring a book to the marketplace. For this I'm indebted to *Dive Training* magazine's managing partner Gary Worden, and publisher Mark Young. Their years of experience in the publishing field and personal commitment to improving diver safety have shown me that it's possible to succeed at business while still maintaining the highest standard for integrity. I also owe a debt to another member of the *Dive Training* team, editor Sean Combs. His constant reminder to "write to divers, not scientists" helped me keep my focus and bring what I hope is a unique perspective to this book.

Finally, it would be unforgivable to forget the researchers, scientists and fellow divers whose words and ideas I can only hope I did justice to in writing this book. My deep gratitude goes to:

Dr. Bruce Bassett
Dr. Jolie Bookspan
Dr. Peter Bennett
Jim Corry
Billy Deans
Joel Dovenbarger
Mike Emmerman
Dr. R.W. "Bill" Hamilton
Dr. Henry Helmpleman
Karl Huggins
Dr. Jennifer Hunt
Dr. Edward Lanphier
Dr. John Lewis
John Lippmann
Mike Menduno
Dr. Richard Moon

Dr. Tom Neuman
Dan Orr
Dr. Andrew Pilmanis
Dr. Michael Powell
Drew Richardson
Dr. Lee Somers
Dr. Merrill Spencer
Dr. Michael Strauss
Cmdr. Ed Thalmann
Dr. Richard Vann
Dr. James Vorosmarti
Dr. Bruce Wienke
Dr. Peter Wilmshurst
Dr. David Yount

... and John Scott Haldane

Foreword

When I go diving I have two goals: Number one, I want to avoid an accident. Number two, I want to have fun.

Having fun is the easy part.

Avoiding injury can be easy too—as long as we know what to look for. Perhaps more than any other reason, that's why Alex Brylske wrote this book. *Beating the Bends* provides a wealth of life-saving information in a succinct and easy-to-understand format.

What is perceived as a diving danger—and what is really dangerous—are usually very different. Think back to when you became a scuba diver (or, if you're thinking about taking up diving, think about your perceptions right now). If you're like most folks, you probably thought the biggest diving hazards were marine life—namely sharks—or drowning, especially if you're not a good swimmer.

During the dive training process, we learn that marine life poses almost no threat. (Marine life, however, can't say the same about us.) Additionally, a fear of the water subsides when you have a tank full of air on your back, plus equipment designed to make up for less-than-expert swimming skills.

In practice, we find that the things that can really harm divers are more subtle than sharks. Fortunately, almost all of these dangers are within our control.

The root of most diving dangers is ignorance. Even though basic scuba courses introduce much of the information divers need to know, there's still a lot to be learned. Experience shows that too many of us consider the dive training process complete when we receive a certification card. That is a mistake that can have serious consequences.

Decompression sickness (DCS) is one subject, in particular, that is not completely addressed during the initial certification course. Granted, many—but certainly not all—divers understand that DCS is a function of pressure and nitrogen gas absorption. Some also know that dive tables and dive computers contain data that can be used to help avoid DCS (although practical experience shows that most divers have difficulty using the tables or don't completely understand the read-outs of their computers). An even smaller group comprehends the correlation between ascent rates, safety stops, and avoiding diving injuries.

In other words, most scuba divers venture into the water with a less-than-adequate understanding of DCS and how to avoid it—perhaps the most fundamental of dive safety issues.

To be safe divers, we must not only memorize dive safety guidelines, but also understand how they have been developed. More importantly, we must incorporate them into our dives to the extent that they become second nature.

That's why *Beating the Bends* is such an important book. It picks up where most diving texts leave off. It provides a history of how decompression safety guidelines have been developed. More importantly, *Beating the Bends* provides easy-to-understand recommendations on how you can reduce your chances of getting the bends. The book is designed to be used over and over again. You'll find yourself referring to it before your dive vacation, reviewing it during continuing scuba education class, and sharing it with your diving friends.

Alex Brylske is uniquely qualified to write on this topic. He has a special talent for making complex technical subjects—such as decompression sickness—easy to understand. Alex combines his writing skills with more than 20 years of experience as a scuba educator. In addition to his role as technical editor for *Dive Training* magazine, Alex continues to train divers and scuba instructors around the world. He is out there, in the field, fighting the battle against diving ignorance on a daily basis. He sees the problems—and solutions—first hand. Those life-saving observations and tips are the core of *Beating the Bends*.

Beating the bends involves more than just avoiding deep, long dives. It's a common-sense process that begins before we even enter the water. The first step in that process is education—and for safety-conscious divers, that starts by reading *Beating the Bends*.

Sean Combs
Editor, *Dive Training* Magazine

Preface

The human body has no use for free-form nitrogen. That's a physiological fact that's irrelevant to most human beings on the planet—but not to those of us who venture under water. Because it takes no part in the metabolic process, whatever nitrogen we breathe in, we must eventually breathe out again. While that may sound simple, it becomes an enormously complex process when, as divers, we breathe air under constantly varying pressures.

Under certain conditions, excess nitrogen released when we ascend generates bubbles, and the disorder we call decompression sickness (DCS), or "the bends," occurs. So, you might think if we could only identify and avoid these conditions then we could prevent the bends. Unfortunately, as testament to the wondrously fickle human machine, it's not that easy. No matter what we do, or how well we prepare, every dive carries with it some risk of bends. The only way we can absolutely avoid it is not to dive.

Assuming no one reading this book would accept that option, I felt a reasonable compromise between not diving and getting the bends might be to write a book that would help divers understand DCS better. But, frankly, you can significantly reduce your bends risk by just following the short list of suggestions contained in the Introduction. So why should I bother writing an entire book, particularly considering there are so many books—or portions of books—on the subject already?

In reviewing the existing material on DCS—and in talking to more divers than I care to count—I came to three conclusions. First, while voluminous information on the bends does exist within the scientific world, much of it never makes its way to the general diving public.

Second, what does make its way to the recreational diver tends to be either extremely basic or so complex that you need a year of medical school to understand it. Oversimplifying the subject prevents divers from developing a full insight into DCS and robs us of the chance to appreciate this fascinating physiological process. Making it too complex simply means that a lot of books and articles remain unread and collect dust on the bookshelves of divers who thought they were interested in learning more. Neither, in my view, makes much of a contribution to making diving safer.

My third conclusion was that no single source treats the subject in a way that is comprehensive yet understandable. You can, for example, find texts that cover the basics or show you how to use a particular dive table. Some books delve deeply into the physiology and medicine of DCS. And a myriad other works deal with particular subjects, such as dive computers, first aid measures, and deep-diving procedures. But nothing has attempted to incorporate what I consider to be all aspects—both theoretical and practical—of the decompression issue from the perspective of the average recreational diver. That's what I have attempted in *Beating the Bends*. I hope it will be a helpful addition to the discussion of diving safety, and that you will find it useful in getting the most out of your underwater experiences.

Dive smart and dive safe,

Alex Brylske
Arcadia, Florida
January 1995

Introduction

If You Read Nothing Else in This Book, Please Read This!

As an educator, I know all too well that people often buy a book with the best of intentions to read it from cover to cover. But unless it's a novel—and a darn good one at that—seldom do we read books that way. We tend to read technical books selectively, concentrating on what interests us or what we need for a particular purpose. I expect that many of you will read *Beating the Bends* in that way.

What I would like you to understand, however, is that some things in this book are too important to miss. With this in mind, I have decided to hit you over the head, at least figuratively, with those aspects of decompression safety that I think are essential. I hope that this will encourage you to read more about why these "ten commandments" are so vital to your safety. But even if you don't care to know about the reasons, at least heed the advice. Please.

The Ten Commandments of Decompression Safety

1. **Avoid maximum limits.** No matter what your table or computer tells you, begin your ascent at least 5 to 10 minutes before reaching the no-decompression limit. Think of approaching these limits as though you were running up to the edge of a cliff. The farther away you are when you stop, the less chance you have of going over.

2. **Always ascend slowly and take a safety stop.** Never ascend faster that 60 feet per minute, (slower is even better), and before surfacing take a safety stop for 3 to 5 minutes at 10 to 20 feet. Remember the cliff analogy. You could walk right up to the preci-

pice—even dangle your toes over the edge—and you probably wouldn't fall off. But, you would greatly reduce your chances of tumbling off if you just took a step or two back away from the edge. That's what a safety stop does—it's the diver's version of backing away from the edge. There's really no such thing as a "no-decompression" dive. Even if you don't have to make a required decompression stop, your ascent itself is a form of decompression.

3. **Avoid dives that require decompression stops.** Because they require extensive planning and support, dives requiring decompression stops are extremely dangerous for recreational divers. In fact, it violates the very definition of "recreational diving" (no-stop diving, no deeper than 130 feet). Even taking the appropriate precautions won't eliminate a higher-than-normal risk of DCS compared with no-stop diving. Many researchers believe the popular models used today to predict no-stop diving are inadequate for predicting profiles requiring stops. While other disagree, the point is nobody knows for sure. All that's certain is that statistically the risk of DCS increases significantly when you exceed no-stop limits.

4. **Avoid high-risk profiles.** While science still argues the reasons why such practices are dangerous, practical experience shows that certain profiles are more likely than others to get you a trip to a recompression chamber. In particular, take care not to dive reverse (a shallow followed by a deep dive) or sawtooth (lots of ups and downs) profiles. On a multilevel dive, spend the first part of your excursion in the deeper range, then move to shallow. Never return to deeper water once you've come up to the shallower range.

5. **Avoid diving when you are dehydrated or when you feel less than 100 percent.** Diving with the proper level of hydration is one of the most important steps you can take in reducing your DCS risk. Thirst is a poor indicator of your state of hydration. Drink water (not soda, coffee, or, worst of all, alcohol) until your urine is copious and virtually colorless. Also avoid diving if you feel tired, sick, or hung over. There will always be another day to go diving, but the consequences of the bends could be with you forever.

6. **Avoid heavy exercise before, during, and after diving.** If you can't avoid heavy exertion while you're in the water, at least take it into account. Plan your decompression status by assuming your dive is 10 feet deeper than your actual depth. Remember, your last decompression stop is on the surface, so rest once you're out of the water. Avoid heavy exercise, such as free-diving, between repetitive dives.

7. **Wear proper exposure protection.** Being cold is one of the contributing factors to DCS that we can do something about. Avoid diving if you feel cold, and if you get chilled while diving, get out of the water. Don't wait until you start shivering. A good general guideline is to wear more exposure protection than you think you'll need. And this isn't just a concern for cold-water divers. All divers lose heat unless the water temperature is above 90 degrees F.

8. **Be extra careful when making multiday, repetitive dives.** No decompression model so far has been designed and tested conclusively for multiple day, multiple dive use. Yet, this is exactly the kind of diving sport divers do—particularly while vacationing at dive resorts. Statistical evidence from the Divers Alert Network raises serious concern over this issue. DAN's data suggest that those at highest risk for DCS are those who make multiday, repetitive dives. To reduce your risk, follow either one of these guidelines: *1) Curtail diving somewhat toward the end of your trip;* or *2) take a day off in the middle of your trip to go sightseeing or just lay on the beach.* Either practice will help reduce your nitrogen levels and, hopefully, your risk of DCS while on a diving vacation.

9. **Know when it's safe to fly.** Because so little data exist about the risks of flying—and driving to altitude—after diving, this has been a controversial subject. You can find the current recommendation for flying after diving in Chapter Five, page 102. Follow it.

10. **Take responsibility for your own safety and accept that not all DCS is avoidable.** An alarming trend in our society is the reluctance to accept personal responsibility for our actions. The credo seems to be: When something goes wrong, blame anyone or anything but ourselves. In reality, it's not our government, not our employers, not our instructors, and not even our mothers who are responsible for our safety. In the final analysis, the buck stops with us—human beings with free will to make a decision and accept the consequences. The other issue that's tough to accept is that you can get DCS even if you do everything right. If, however, you accept the risk of being a diver (or driving a car or even getting out of bed in the morning), then that's life and sometimes life just ain't fair. We may someday understand the nuances of the human body well enough to know everything there is to know about the bends. But we're not there yet—not by a long shot—so the best we can do today is make informed decisions based on the best possible evidence...and perhaps say a little prayer.

CHAPTER ONE

SCUBA—Some Come Up Bubbling A lot

A Primer on Decompression Sickness

What you learned about decompression sickness (DCS) in your beginning scuba course, although conceptually accurate, was probably oversimplified. It's a lot more involved—and much more interesting—than the often-used analogy of opening up a shaken bottle of soda.

We should begin any discussion of DCS by stating that it is a complicated and poorly understood disorder. In fact, while the average diver may feel he or she knows precisely what causes DCS, that certainty is not shared by the scientific community.

Even though a great deal of new information has come to light in recent years, significant questions remain about how DCS really works. To this day no one knows for sure. Despite the uncertainty, there are lots of ideas; and this chapter presents a thorough review of the current theories researchers and physiologists propose to explain DCS.

We'll explore the interaction of liquids and gases under pressure, and explain the terms *gas tension, pressure gradient, saturation*, and *supersaturation*. We'll then move on to how the human body is affected by these physical phenomena, and why people are far more prone to "bubbling" than a simple glass of water.

Moving past the pure mechanics of bubble formation, we'll discuss important biochemical changes caused by DCS, as well as the role of blood flow, tissue density, and other factors that may contribute to a diver's susceptibility to the bends. In the final segment, we'll look at some theories researchers use to explain the varied symptomatology of DCS and introduce you to a relatively new term in the diving medical community—*decompression illness*.

GASES AND LIQUIDS

Before we can understand how DCS occurs, we must review some basic ideas on how gases are absorbed and eliminated in liquids.

To the naked eye, a liquid does not appear to have any space in it to allow gas to enter. However, we all have direct experience to the contrary—gases can dissolve into liquids *[Figure 1-1A]*. We're reminded

FIGURE 1-1

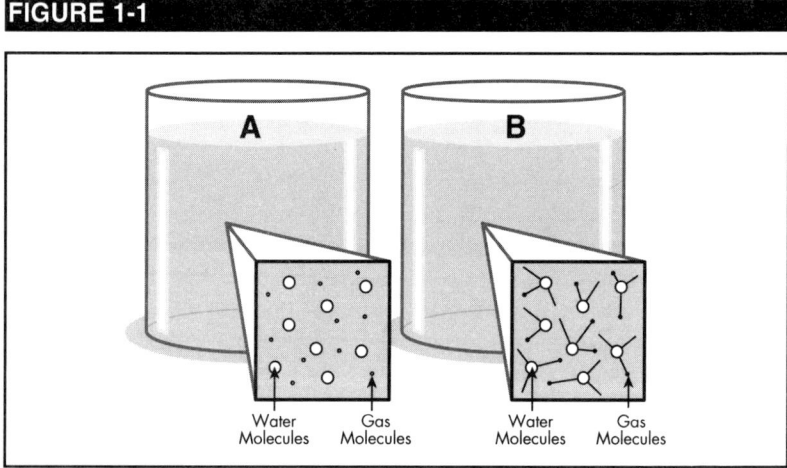

A: Just as sugar can dissolve into coffee, gas can dissolve into a liquid. Ample room exists between the water molecules for gas molecules to occupy. *B:* Though dissolved in a liquid, a gas behaves no differently than if it were in any other container. Whether confined within a balloon or dissolved within a liquid, the gas still exerts pressure.

of this every time we pour a can of soda into a glass of ice. The profuse formation of gas bubbles, or *effervescence*, is merely carbon dioxide being released from the liquid. The gas, although not visible in its dissolved form, remains in solution until something acts on it to make it come out.

Furthermore, not only do gases dissolve into liquids, they also continue exerting pressure while in the solution. This internal pressure is called *gas tension [Figure 1-1B]*.

Exactly how much gas a liquid will absorb, and what factors affect this absorption, was first studied in the 18th century by Scottish scientist William Henry. His experiments showed the amount of gas that dissolves into a liquid at a given temperature depends on the pressure of the gas in contact with the liquid. This is called Henry's Law, and you've probably experienced it firsthand many times. Have you ever been to a party where there's a keg of beer? When it's first tapped, it tastes great—fresh and just the right amount of carbonation. But what about later? As the keg begins to run dry, the beer starts to taste flat. That's Henry's Law at work. At first, the keg contained a lot of pressure. So a lot of gas—in this case carbon dioxide—was able to dissolve into the beer. As the keg was drained, less gas was available to dissolve into the beer; hence, the flat taste.

Henry's Law further tells us that both pressure and temperature affect how gas dissolves into liquid. Let's see how this might happen. Imagine you have a beaker of water with absolutely no gas dissolved in it. The beaker is inside a chamber where a perfect vacuum exists. This means that absolutely no gas is in contact with the water. (These conditions are impossible to achieve except perhaps in outer space, but it makes the concept easier to understand.) If air enters the chamber and comes in contact with the water, air molecules begin dissolving into the water. The gas in the water then exerts a pressure, or gas tension.

Gas will continue dissolving into liquid until the gas tension equalizes with the air pressure in contact with the liquid. But this takes time. The difference between the air pressure in contact with the liquid and the gas tension within the liquid is called a *pressure gradient*. If the pressure gradient is high, gas is absorbed into the liquid quickly. But, as the gas molecules continue dissolving into the liquid, the gradient begins to decrease. So, molecules dissolve more slowly.

Over time the gas tension in the liquid equals the air pressure in contact with the liquid. Although molecules continue to pass between the liquid/air interface, no net exchange of gas occurs. The liquid is now saturated. (Purists prefer the term *equilibrate* to *saturate*, but we'll use the latter, more familiar term).

Let's now pressurize the vacuum chamber. This increases the pressure of the gas in contact with the water, and causes even more gas to dissolve, as illustrated by *Figure 1-2A*. Over time, gas continues entering the water until the gas tension in the liquid and the air pressure on the liquid are equal (saturation), as shown by *Figure 1-2B*. As Henry's Law predicts, the more pressure the gas exerts on the water, the more gas dissolves into the water.

FIGURE 1-2

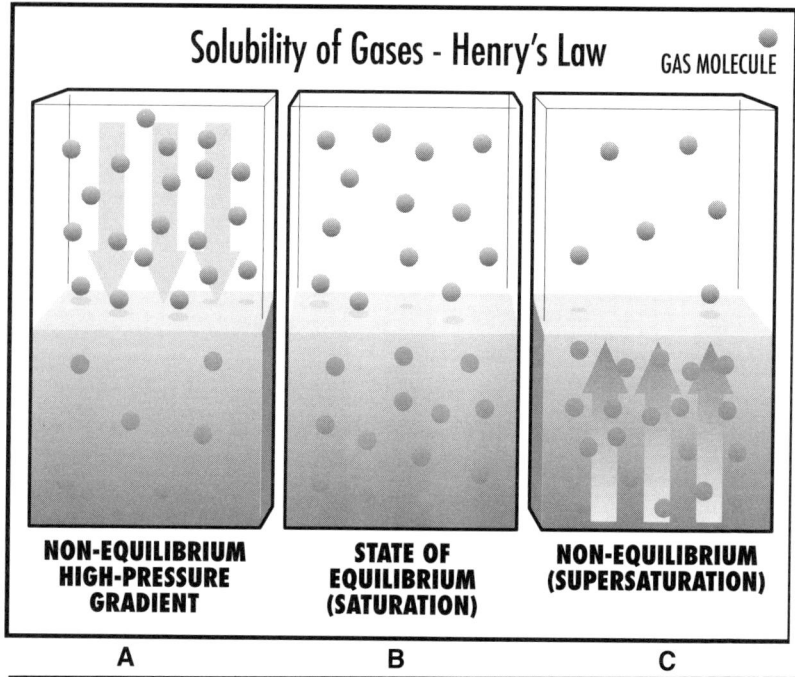

Solubility of Gases - Henry's Law

GAS MOLECULE

NON-EQUILIBRIUM HIGH-PRESSURE GRADIENT

STATE OF EQUILIBRIUM (SATURATION)

NON-EQUILIBRIUM (SUPERSATURATION)

A   B   C

If we release the pressure in the chamber the phenomenon is reversed. With less pressure on the water, the gas dissolved in it has a greater gas tension than the air in contact with the water. As *Figure 1-2C* shows, the water now contains more gas than it can keep in solution at that pressure. This condition is called *supersaturation*.

Gas transfers out of the liquid until the gas tension is equal to the air pressure. If air pressure is reduced very slowly, if the water isn't shaken, or if no foreign particles are present, the gas transfer is undetectable—no gas bubbles form. But, if the air pressure decreases too quickly, or the water is vigorously shaken, or foreign particles are added to the water, the gas begins escaping more rapidly—so quickly that, like a shaken bottle of soda, the gas molecules form visible bubbles.

In addition to pressure, temperature affects gas absorption into liquid. Heat makes the molecules of a liquid accelerate. This rapid movement leaves less space between the liquid molecules for gas molecules to occupy, so fewer gas molecules can dissolve into or remain in the liquid. We see this when we boil water. As the water begins to heat, small air bubbles form and collect at the bottom of the container. They are caused by the sped-up molecules pushing dissolved gas out of the water. It makes sense, then, that cooler liquids can hold more dissolved gas than warmer liquids. A cooler liquid contains slower molecules, allowing room for more gas molecules to occupy.

Gas dissolves into blood and other tissues just as air dissolved into our beaker of water. As we shall see next, however, some important differences exist between body tissues and a beaker of water.

Applying Physics to Physiology

You now have a good general understanding of the phenomenon of gas absorption into liquids, but it doesn't exactly explain how gas bubbles form in our bodies. To understand the mechanism of DCS, we must begin by exploring the differences between a beaker of water and the human body.

Because of special bonding characteristics, water molecules are difficult to separate. This gives water a high tensile strength, a measure of a substance's resistance to being torn apart or cracked. This characteristic makes spontaneous bubble formation in water difficult. For example, you could theoretically compress a beaker of pure water to more than 200 atmospheres and—provided you didn't shake it—immediately decompress it without forming a single bubble.

But wait a minute. If that's true, why does a bottle of soda—with pressure far less that 200 atmospheres—fizz when it's opened? And more importantly, why can't a diver ascend from as shallow as 33 feet (2 atmospheres) without the risk of the bubble formation we call DCS? The answers to these important questions go to the heart of modern theories of decompression sickness.

The fact that pure water has such incredible resistance to bubble formation tells us that something else besides supersaturation produces bubbles. Otherwise, pure water couldn't tolerate the incredible decompression from more than 200 atmospheres. A hint at the answer comes from our description of water in the example. Notice that we said *pure* water, not just any water.

It's important that the liquid being compressed contain no impurities or substances other than water molecules. We can see why this is the case by looking at another phenomenon involving water—rain. We've all known from childhood that rain comes from clouds, which are made up of water vapor. But how does a raindrop evolve from water vapor? At the core of every raindrop is a particle of dust that acts as a *"seed"*—a point around which the water vapor collects and grows into a drop. Now let's apply this idea to bubble formation.

If we repeat the experiment using a liquid containing other substances or particles along with water molecules, we'll see a big difference from the experiment using pure water. Just like with raindrops, foreign particles in the water seed the production of gas bubbles. Exactly how many bubbles form depends on the number of particles dissolved in the liquid, the pressure differential, and other factors. The point is, the seeds make the difference.

You can confirm this prediction in your own kitchen. First, pour a can of soda into a glass. (No ice, please.) Allow it to stand for several hours. Pretty flat by now, huh? Without disturbing it, drop a pinch of salt into the glass. What you'll see is that the supposed "flat" soda can still produce bubbles if something acts as a seed for those bubbles. This proves there are factors other than supersaturation that cause bubble formation.

But what does this have to do with human DCS? We don't have "seeds" in us, do we? Actually, humans have lots of "seeds," more accurately termed *gas micronuclei*. These are microscopic pockets of gas caused by various factors, including movement. If you think back to our experiment with the beaker of pure water, you'll remember we said that the beaker wasn't shaken. The turbulence caused by shaking the water causes micronuclei to appear. They seed the formation of bubbles, and our experiment would have a different outcome. If you don't believe this, try vigorously shaking your next can of soda before you open it. (Better have a rag or sponge ready.)

Obviously, our blood is not motionless. Nor is our body. When we dive, our muscles are in constant motion. This continual movement, combined with the normal turbulence of blood flow, is one current theory behind gas seed formation in humans. During an ascent from depth, nitrogen diffuses into these seeds (which are actually areas of low pressure), forming tiny micro bubbles.

This phenomenon tends to occur in the capillaries—the smallest structures of the circulatory system. From there, many of the bubbles enter the venous circulation and flow back to the heart. Because they are very tiny bubbles, they normally do not cause any blockage in the vessels during their transit. From the heart, blood travels to the lungs. When the bubbles reach the extremely fine capillary bed of the alveoli (air sacs of the lungs), they are trapped. The bubbles diffuse back into the alveoli, and nitrogen gas is expired in the normal respiratory process. Because these bubbles have no effect on us, they are called *subclinical* or *asymptomatic*. We also know them as "silent bubbles." But what about the bubbles that don't make their way back to the lungs?

To understand the next aspect of bubble formation, let's go back to that glass of soda you left standing in your kitchen. You saw that by adding a pinch of salt you could make more bubbles, even after the soda was flat. Now place a candle in the glass. Bubbles immediately form all around it. This happens because the candle (paraffin wax) is a nonwettable or hydrophobic substance *[Photo 1-1]*. Bubbles occur quickly on nonwettable surfaces because they require less energy to form than on a wettable surface. What does this have to do with bubble formation in us? According to some researchers, everything.

PHOTO 1-1

The immersed candle experiment shows how easy it is for bubbles to form on the surface of a nonwettable or hydrophobic substance.

Like wax, the interior surfaces of our blood vessels are nonwettable. These walls are not smooth, as you might imagine, but highly irregular. They are made up of tissues that are primarily lipid (fat), and as we know, "Oil and water don't mix." This similarity to the candle experiment, according to some researchers, goes a long way in explaining bubble formation in divers.

As the diver ascends and continues offgasing, the bubbles grow. Interestingly, they tend not to form the familiar spherical shape. Instead, they become elongated—a shape that increases their surface area and resistance to movement. Bubbles in blood vessels can stop or interfere with normal blood flow. This further compounds the decompression process because dissolved nitrogen has a more difficult time escaping from the tissues *[Figure 1-3]*.

Dr. Michael Powell, a well-known decompression researcher, describes this phenomenon as the "bottleneck effect." The dissolved nitrogen tries to escape or wash out, but the localized bubble forma-

FIGURE 1-3

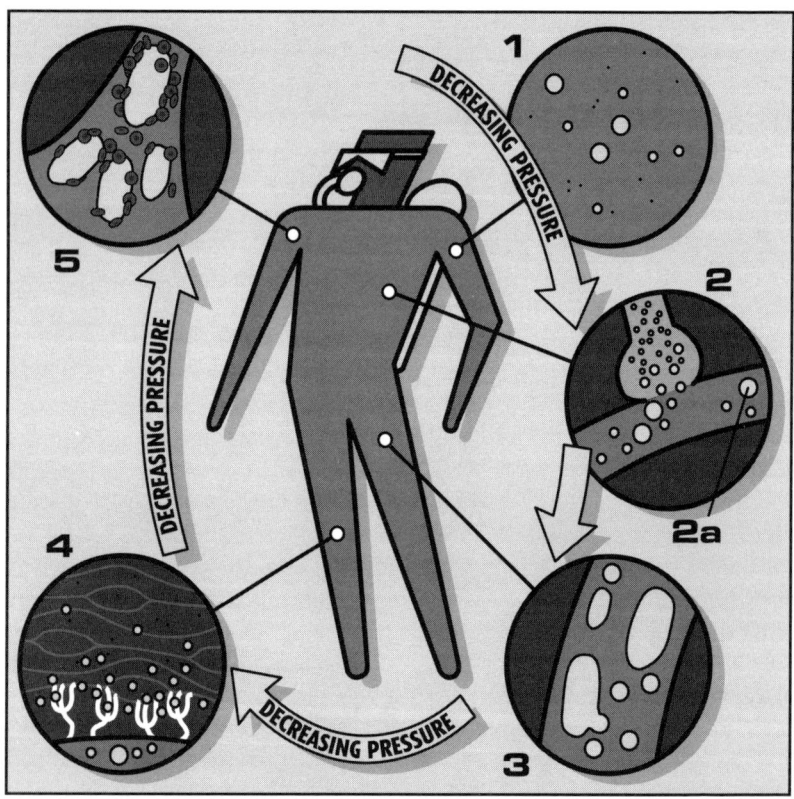

1. As a diver ascends, nitrogen diffuses into "gas seeds," forming "microbubbles." Some of these microbubbles are transported through the heart and into the capillary beds of the lungs. 2. Once in the capillary beds, microbubbles are trapped. The bubbles are diffused and exit the body through normal respiration; hence, the term "silent bubbles." If there are so few bubbles that they can be "scrubbed" by the lungs, some forms of DCS might not occur. 2a. However, if there is too much nitrogen in a diver's tissues, or the diver ascends too quickly, more bubbles form. Numerous bubbles may not be absorbed and could remain in the circulatory system...3. As bubbles grow, they become elongated. Smaller microbubbles start diffusing into larger ones. 4. Meanwhile, gas seeds in ligaments and tendons attract escaping nitrogen gas. The result is extravascular bubbles, which, if large enough, pinch nerves. The consequence is the classic joint pain of DCS. 5. Back in the circulatory system, nitrogen bubbles grow and attract blood platelets. Blood vessels constrict. Complement proteins are released, causing blood volume to plummet. The bubbles and biochemical reactions hinder blood flow.

FIGURE 1-4

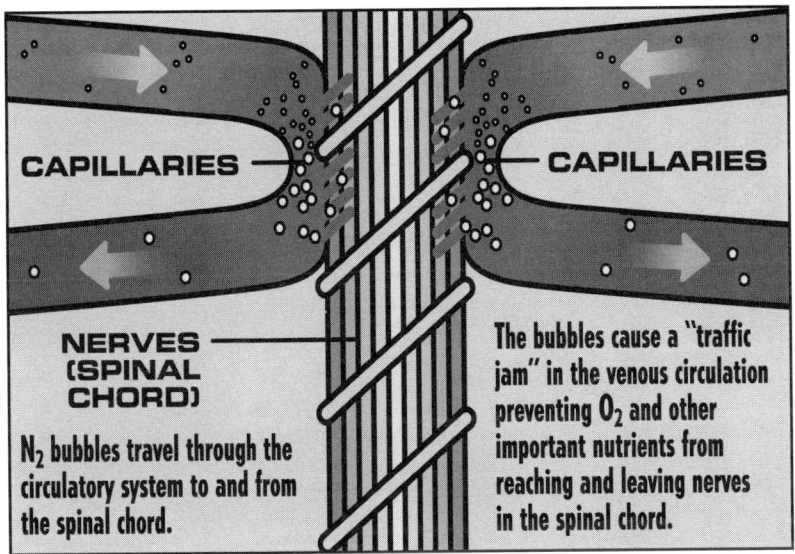

CAPILLARIES

CAPILLARIES

NERVES (SPINAL CHORD)

N₂ bubbles travel through the circulatory system to and from the spinal chord.

The bubbles cause a "traffic jam" in the venous circulation preventing O₂ and other important nutrients from reaching and leaving nerves in the spinal chord.

tion impedes the flow of blood that would otherwise carry away the dissolved nitrogen *[Figure 1-4]*. The nitrogen has to go somewhere, so it diffuses into the newly formed bubbles, causing them to grow even larger. This mechanism is believed to be a primary cause of neurologic DCS (described in more detail later in this chapter).

Unfortunately, bubbles don't just form within the blood vessels. Nitrogen can diffuse into seeds between tissues. In this case, the bubbles can distort and permanently damage the tissue. As they grow, the bubbles also put pressure on nerves. This type of bubble formation is called *extravascular*, meaning "outside the vessel."

Aqueous (watery) tissues—the type that make up ligaments and joints—are especially prone to developing extravascular bubbles; this is one reason for the widely held theory that extravascular bubbling is the primary mechanism for joint pain, one of the classic symptoms of DCS. (The other classic symptom involving the limbs is often described as a "deep pain," which is difficult to describe and unaffected by movement. Theory holds that this pain is caused by bubbles in the circulation of the bone, which result in either a reduced blood supply—a condition called *ischemia*—or an increase in pressure inside the bone cavity.)

Fat (lipid) tissue has an affinity for forming extravascular bubbles, as well. In fact, because fatty tissues can hold five times the amount of nitrogen than can an equal quantity of aqueous tissue, lipid tissues might serve as reservoirs for extravascular bubbles. Some researchers have shown experimentally that high enough quantities of these bubbles can result in vascular hemorrhage, thus forcing both the bubbles and the fat tissue into the bloodstream.

The final complicating factor in bubble formation involves the effect on decompression models. All existing tables and most computers used by recreational divers assume that gas remains in solution at all times. But as we've seen, this is not always the case.

Statistics from the Divers Alert Network (DAN) indicate that perhaps as many as 70 to 90 percent of all divers "bubble" during the course of a week of diving. The reliability of a decompression model must decrease if one of its most important assumptions—gas re-

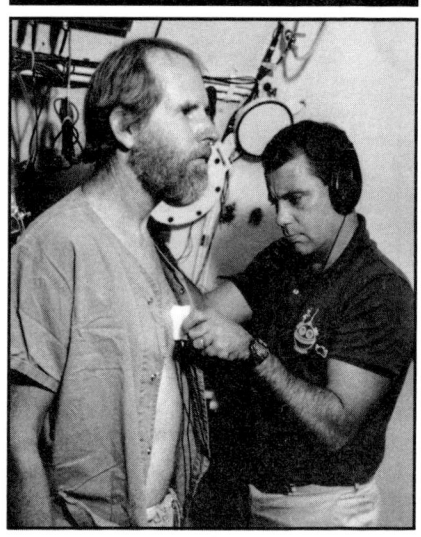

PHOTO 1-2

The Doppler Detector works by transmitting high-frequency sound waves into the body. The waves bounce off any circulating bubbles and produce distinctive sound signatures, which are interpreted by experienced operators. Many believe that silent bubbles are a precursor to DCS; and by keeping these bubbles to a minimum, a diver can reduce the risk of DCS. Others dispute this theory.

mains in solution at all times—does not hold true. This should be a powerful reason for divers to abide by DAN's recommendations for multi-day repetitive diving. These recommendations include: 1) avoid repetitive dives deeper than 80 feet; and 2) when on a diving vacation, take a day off in mid-week or curtail diving a bit toward the end [*Photo 1-2].*

It Ain't Just Mechanics

Based on the simplistic explanation they receive in their training, most divers assume that DCS is caused simply from the mechanics of bubbles growing in the blood and tissues. In reality, the mechanism of

PHOTO 1-3

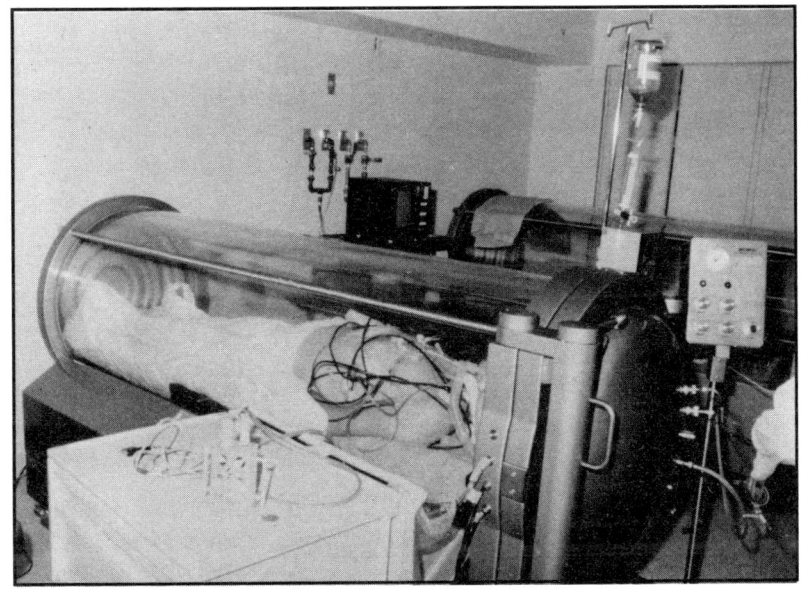

Recompression is only one part of the treatment for DCS. Intravenous drug therapy to counteract any biochemical complications is another.

DCS involves a highly complex interplay of both bubble mechanics and biochemistry. During treatment, in fact, dealing with the biochemical complications of DCS is just as important as recompression *[Photo 1-3].*

About 25 years ago a researcher named Chyssanthou showed that a substance in the blood called *smooth muscle activating factor* caused inflammation and could induce the bends in decompressed animals. He also found that a substance called *anti-smooth muscle activating factor* had just the opposite effect. He was unable to induce DCS in animals to which he gave the anti-smooth muscle activating factor; and the substance tended to resolve symptoms in animals that were bent. These findings led to further studies into the immunological involvement of DCS.

Other researchers showed that gas bubble formation brings on important changes in blood chemistry. The presence of bubbles in the blood activates the clotting process. Platelets—blood components responsible for clotting—become sticky, attaching themselves to each other and the newly formed bubbles.

The bubbles also cause inflammation of the capillary walls, causing leakage of fluid into the tissues, which contributes to dehydration. (This phenomenon is known as *third spacing*.) Eventually, the blood vessels themselves start breaking down. This dislodges fat particles into the blood, and these particles are yet another possible origin of gas seeds.

Recent studies have also shown that bubble formation activates substances called *complement proteins* (C3a and C5a). This causes the release of histamines and other chemicals that also cause fluid to leak from the capillaries into the surrounding tissues. (Localized swelling caused by this fluid release is termed *edema*.) This process, incidentally, is similar to the way the body reacts when it goes into shock.

Furthermore, animal experiments have shown that if the release of these complement proteins is stopped, the severity of DCS lessens. From this evidence, researchers hypothesize that a person's susceptibility to DCS may depend on how easily the body releases these substances. The implication of this line of research is exciting; perhaps we can someday develop a blood test to identify divers prone to DCS.

Recently, a researcher named Butler has shown that when DCS bubbles come into contact with white blood cells, the cells release a toxin called an *oxygen radical*. This substance also causes inflammation, which further slows the blood.

The overall effect of this biochemical activity is like a snowball rolling downhill: the blood thickens, becomes sticky, and cannot move as efficiently through the vessels; red blood cells now clump or "sludge" together; this, in turn, decreases circulatory efficiency and nitrogen wash-out; more bubbles form, and bubbles that already exist grow; the blood flow slows even further, and the condition gets worse.

Factors that Complicate the Process

Two factors determine how gas is delivered to tissues. One factor is the amount of blood flow the tissues receive, known as *perfusion*. Brain and muscle tissues are well-perfused—they get lots of blood and, therefore, lots of gas. Bone and fat tissues have a poorer supply of blood. This means they get less gas than well-perfused tissues.

The second factor is how gas is transferred throughout the tissues once it gets there. This is called *diffusion*. Individual cells are not made of a uniform substance (like gelatin, for example). Instead, cells contain tiny structures called *organelles*, which are responsible for metabolic processes. This complicates predicting the transfer of gas across a tissue.

As if these factors do not confuse the picture enough, there's one more. No matter how well we may someday be able to describe these phenomena, we each still have a unique anatomy and physiology. So, no existing model—regardless of how well it's researched and validated—can describe exactly what is going on inside of us as individuals. Though decompression models cannot take this individuality into account, we can still factor this variability into our decision-making.

Dr. Michael Strauss has put forth an hypothesis about the role altered blood flow has on bends, which he terms *disordered decompression sickness*. His theory is based on the dynamics and control of blood flow. While the average person has about 5-6 liters of blood, the total capacity of the circulatory system is 150 liters. Thus, at any one time, less than one-fifteenth of the blood that could flow to a noncritical tissue is flowing to it. (Critical tissues such as the brain receive a more profuse blood supply.)

Our body regulates the flow of blood in a highly complex and specific manner. When this regulatory process is alerted, impeded, or otherwise "disordered," the result could be DCS. To illustrate the point, Strauss uses an example of a diver going to depth, then placing a tourniquet around his arm. As the venous blood cannot return to his heart, the result would most likely be significant bubble formation and DCS because of the disordered blood flow.

Further, Strauss contends there are three types of disordering events: neurological, cardiovascular, and musculoskeletal. Neurological disordering can be caused by such events as: head injury, air embolism, electrical shock, or any interference with the normal neuro-regulatory process of blood flow. Cardiovascular disordering can result from events such as: heart attack, dysrhythmias (alterations in the heartbeat), hypovolemic shock, and dehydration. Musculoskeletal disordering can occur from traumatic injury, vascular embarrassment, strenuous exercise or fatigue. All of these conditions can result in altered or disordered blood flow that can lead to DCS.

DCS Susceptibility Factors

For years researchers and clinicians have suggested that certain individual factors or physiologic attributes make individuals more or less prone to DCS. These are often called susceptibility or predisposition factors. Most of these factors involve some alteration of normal blood flow (perfusion), which affects the absorption or elimination of nitrogen. While little clinical evidence exists that correlates these factors with a measurable increase in the risk of DCS, common sense says certain conditions and practices will probably increase the risk to some degree. Let's take a look at some of these factors.

Age: The aging process causes a decrease in the efficiency of all biologic systems, including circulation and respiration. Logically, this means a decrease in the efficient exchange of all gases, including nitrogen. So, if all other factors are equal, an older diver will tend to be more susceptible to DCS than a younger one.

Dehydration: This is perhaps one of the biggest factors influencing the onset of DCS; and, more importantly, it's a factor we can do something about. First, the theory. Dehydration "thickens" the blood by reducing its volume and slowing the flow rate. The assumption is that less efficient circulation alters nitrogen absorption and elimination. This slowing, or *stasis* as it's termed medically, could allow nitrogen, which might otherwise remain in solution under normal blood-flow conditions, to coalesce into bubbles; and it could allow silent bubbles to grow into symptomatic bubbles. Adding credence to the dehydration theory is a study done several years ago in which a researcher purposely induced DCS in rats, then resolved their symptoms simply by giving them plasma and intravenous fluids.

The dehydration mechanism is analogous to another phenomenon in nature—how water freezes A fast-moving stream will not freeze, even though the ambient temperature may be below freezing. Yet, under the same temperature conditions, a still body of water will freeze. Thus, the state was affected dramatically by no other factor than its movement. This same concept may apply to blood flow and supersaturated nitrogen. One of the most important factors influencing the blood's flow rate is its density.

A diver must never forget that diving robs moisture from the body in ways that we're not even aware of—be it the profuse sweating from putting on an exposure suit, re-moistening the extremely dry air from a scuba tank as we breathe, or the significantly increased urine output due to immersion, divers fight a constant battle to maintain a normal state of hydration. One way to monitor your hydration state is to keep an eye on your urine. If it's clear and virtually colorless, you're well-hydrated. If it's dark or cloudy, you're not. That's a sure sign that you need to drink more fluids.

Injuries and illness: Like dehydration, both of these conditions can alter normal circulatory efficiency. Evidence also points to a greater

PHOTO 1-4

PHOTO 1-5

Remaining well-hydrated is one of the most important precautions you can take to avoid DCS. Always drink plenty of water or other noncarbonated beverages before diving.

Maintaining body heat is another way many believe you can reduce the risk of DCS. A good rule of thumb is to wear more exposure protection than you think you'll need. A hood is particularly effective in helping you conserve heat.

likelihood of decompression sickness in divers who have experienced the disorder previously.

Anxiety: A person's psychological state has a definite effect upon physiology. We're all aware, for example, how our heart races when we are frightened. (This is because adrenaline is released into the blood). That means there's an increase in your circulatory rate that can alter normal gas exchange.

Drugs and alcohol: Although no relationship between alcohol and DCS has ever been proven in a controlled scientific study, common sense tells us that risk increases for anyone who consumes alcohol before diving. The theory goes like this: Alcohol consumption increases blood flow in the peripheral circulation; therefore, drinking before diving could cause a greater nitrogen absorption than what's predicted by the dive tables or computer. This might increase susceptibility to DCS even if you are within the table or computer limits.

Furthermore, drinking can promote DCS in other ways. Alcohol is a diuretic—it makes you urinate. This loss of fluid can contribute to dehydration. The brain is especially susceptible to dehydration from alcohol consumption. This is why a headache is the most common symptom of a hangover. The effect of dehydration lasts even longer than the headache. From this, some researchers suggest that imbibing divers are at an increased risk of not merely any type of DCS but neurological DCS—the most serious form of the disorder.

While most divers are aware of the potential dangers of drinking before diving, few understand the possible implications of drinking afterward. Some researchers argue that changes in blood flow caused by drinking after a dive might accelerate the release of nitrogen and indirectly enhance bubble formation.

Other researchers suggest that drinking after diving might contribute directly to bubble formation. This, they contend, is at least theoretically possible because of still another chemical property of alcohol—it reduces surface tension, the tendency for a substance, such as a bubble, to exhibit properties resembling those of a stretched elastic membrane. Surface tension is one of the forces that helps resist bubble growth in DCS. Therefore, reducing it could be a factor in encouraging the growth of bubbles that might otherwise remain too small to cause symptoms of DCS.

The effect of alcohol on bubble growth could be extremely important when we consider how common silent bubbling is in divers. As we saw earlier in this chapter, some studies have indicated that silent (asymptomatic) bubbles may occur in as many as 70 to 90 percent of all divers who engage in multiple, repetitive diving. The possible contribution that alcohol consumption might have on pushing these silent bubbles into the realm of symptomatic bubbles can't be ignored. The conclusion seems clear: Never drink before diving and wait a reasonable period even after diving.

Other drugs—both illicit and prescribed medications—can probably affect the incidence of DCS, particularly if they have some impact on circulation or blood chemistry. The increase in ambient pressure when diving also complicates the issue because it alone can unpredictably alter the effect of some drugs.

Carbon dioxide: Increased levels of carbon dioxide cause dilation of the blood vessels and can alter gas transport. It can also contribute to "sludging" of the blood by making the red cells sticky. Furthermore, most of the carbon dioxide in the blood is carried as an acidic chemical called *bicarbonate*. Some authorities believe the presence of this chemical alone might create an excellent seed for bubble formation. Thus, high levels of carbon dioxide do not help the decompression process, and you should strive to maintain your level within a normal range.

Cold: We saw earlier in this chapter how temperature affects the amount of gas that can dissolve into a liquid. While the body's core temperature remains stable, the temperature of the extremities and peripheral circulation can change significantly. This could alter the normal circulation process and nitrogen solubility. To take the effects of cold into account, a good practice is to assume your dive is 10 feet deeper than actual, and plan you bottom time accordingly.

Heavy exercise: Indications are that exercise may have a very significant impact on the development of DCS in many ways. First, the motion of exercise may help form gas seeds by the friction and low-pressure areas created as tissues and joints rub against each other. Changes in blood-flow dynamics brought on by exercise may also help produce micronuclei. This is explained by phenomena known as *Reynold's cavitation* and *tribonuelation*. Through flow dynamics and friction, these forces cause low-pressure areas throughout the body, which can become the site of micro-bubble formation.

Clear evidence exists that heavy exercise before diving can cause significant silent bubble development. Research with NASA's space-shuttle astronauts has shown that bed rest before a mission is effective in reducing silent bubbling during decompression from the shuttle's 14.7-psi environment to the 4.3-psi internal pressure of a space suit. A prudent conclusion from all this experience might be not only to avoid any strenuous activity—such as a vigorous workout—before diving, but also to rest as much as possible.

Heavy exercise during the dive increases circulation and accelerates uptake of nitrogen. After you stop exercising, outgassing of nitrogen occurs more slowly. Unfortunately, most decompression models assume that ingassing and outgassing occur at the same rate. Additionally, just as it does at the surface, exercising while at depth increases the turbulence of blood and creates low-pressure centers that could increase the number of gas seeds.

Conversely, some researchers believe that a moderate level of exercise might actually assist outgassing of nitrogen during decompression. The trouble is, no one has been able to quantify what a "moderate" level means. In the final analysis, no current decompression model can accurately take into account such variations of circulation. The consensus is to avoid heavy exercise before, during, and even after diving.

Deep diving: Statistical evidence on the relationship of deeper diving to DCS is compelling. Navy divers, for example, show a DCS incidence on deep dives (50-100 feet) nines times that of shallow dives (less than 50 feet). In recreational divers, almost three-quarters of the cases of DCS treated happened to people diving beyond 80 feet.

Obesity: This is another controversial subject. Some authorities say that in sport diving, fat is only important as an indicator of physical conditioning, and physical conditioning is an indication of efficient gas exchange. They further contend that in terms of nitrogen retention, the actual quantity of body fat is probably of little consequence to recreational divers. This is because fat is such a "slow" tissue, it's unlikely to affect divers who restrict themselves to no-decompression profiles.

Other researchers believe obesity could be a significant factor in a diver's susceptibility to DCS. Obese people tend to have high blood lipid levels. As described earlier in this chapter, this might increase susceptibility to the bends. We do know for certain that nitrogen has a much higher affinity for fat than other tissues, but how this impacts the occurrence of DCS is uncertain.

Gender: Women have certain physiologic differences from men that could predispose them to DCS. These differences include a higher body fat ratio than men and possible fluid retention during menstruation. Recent studies, along with analysis of accident reports from DAN, show no apparent difference in susceptibility of DCS between men and women. This question, however, has not yet been definitively answered.

Vacation behavior: Unfortunately, diving and vacationing often do not mix well. The rigors of diving three or more times a day requires that you get adequate rest, nutrition, and avoid excessive alcohol intake. Otherwise, you can compromise your circulation efficiency. In particular, with multilevel, multiday diving, inadequate rest and excessive partying have been shown statistically to be contributing factors to DCS. Although no one is expecting you to live the life of a monk while on vacation, you must use common sense to dive safely. And the more diving you expect to do, the more caution you should exercise.

Understanding Symptoms

Each year 650,000 Americans die from heart disease. About half of these victims succumb to a sudden attack outside the hospital setting. Many of these deaths could be prevented if the victim were to get immediate medical attention. Why don't they seek help earlier? The answer is often that the victim either denies the symptoms ("Oh, it's just indigestion.") or has no idea that certain symptoms even indicate a heart problem (nausea or jaw pain, for example).

The encouraging news about heart disease is that compared with statistics from the 1960s, it's declining. This success is credited to improved education. Today people are more likely to be aware of both the early symptoms of a heart attack and the risk factors that can lead to heart disease.

This situation is somewhat analogous to DCS. Ignorance and denial are common reasons for divers delaying treatment or never seeking it in the first place. In fact, in most cases where DCS symptoms are not immediately severe, the diver's initial reaction is to pass the incident off as "just a strained muscle" or "I'm just a little tired." This scenario partly explains the data from DAN that indicates almost 50 percent of divers stricken by DCS wait 12 or more hours before seeking treatment. Some have even waited as long as five days.

While it's difficult to do much about the denial of DCS symptoms, we can do something about ignorance. Just as heart attack deaths have declined due to better education, we can also reduce the incidence of DCS through increased knowledge of its causes and symptoms.

All Bends are Not Equal

Many divers are unaware of how soon after diving DCS symptoms tend to appear. Evidence compiled by DAN shows that 66 percent of all DCS symptoms arise within 30 minutes of surfacing; 74 percent within 2 hours; and 95 percent within 24 hours. In rare cases, symptoms have even occurred after as long as three or more days. This long delay occurs particularly in cases where the victim flies soon after diving. In general, cases where symptoms appear soon after diving tend to produce the more serious incidents of DCS. As is the case with many other medical conditions, symptoms generally get worse with delay of treatment. If you suspect you might have symptoms of DCS, seek medical assistance immediately.

While serious symptoms such as extreme pain or paralysis are easy to recognize, many divers are completely unaware of other common symptoms. Two of the most common are a general unwell feeling (malaise) and extreme fatigue. Yet, diving is a rigorous activity and a certain degree of fatigue is expected after a dive. How do you know, then, whether you are just tired or are experiencing symptoms of DCS?

Where Did "Bends" Come From?

Over the years various terms have been used to describe what we today call decompression sickness (DCS) or decompression illness (DCI). Just a few examples from the historical record are: Caisson disease, Diver's Palsy, Tunnel Disease, Aeropathy, Hyperbaric Pneumatosis, Aerebullosis, Pompholyhaemia, and even Luftdruckerkrankungen. But the name we are most familiar with is, of course, the bends. How the disorder came to be known as such is an interesting aside.

In the late nineteenth century, most victims of DCS were not divers but laborers who worked on the sea bed in pressurized enclosures called *caissons*. Those afflicted with noncritical forms of DCS sought relief by walking in an abnormal, contoured manner. As it happened, it was also quite fashionable for ladies of the time to walk in an awkward, forward-leaning stance called the "Grecian Bend." Thus, caisson workers suffering from decompression sickness were said to have the Grecian Bend or simply "the bends."

Whether the term came into common use as a result of the Brooklyn Bridge or St. Louis Bridge project is still disputed. Nonetheless, the term "bends" has obviously stuck.

A good guideline is that you should be suspect if you are fatigued beyond what you might expect from the normal exertion of diving. The exact cause of these symptoms is uncertain. But many researchers suggest that they are due to a general body stress reaction resulting from bubble formation, primarily in the central nervous system.

The symptoms of DCS depend on the amount and location of bubbles. Long ago a general classification scheme came into use based upon the symptoms. DCS that did not show any apparent neurologic involvement was classified as *type I* or so-called "pain-only" bends. Cases with neurologic or other systemic involvement, such as the inability to urinate or paralysis, were called *type II*.

More recently, science has revised the classification system because the differences between a type I and type II event are often difficult to distinguish. Because type I can evolve into type II, the terms also had little meaning in guiding treatment. Furthermore, the old classification of "pain-only" implied that it wasn't as serious as other forms of DCS.

That's all changed; now there's no such thing as a "nonserious" case of DCS. A diver should consider any form of the disorder a serious problem and treat it appropriately. The term "mild" is, in fact, used to describe only cases of DCS involving unwarranted fatigue or itching as the sole symptoms, and where these symptoms resolve merely by breathing pure oxygen. Everything else, included so-called "pain-only" cases, are serious forms of the bends.

The most common symptom of DCS is pain in the joints or limbs. It occurs in about 75 percent of the cases. The exact mechanism of what causes this pain is uncertain, although we related two theories earlier in this chapter. Joint pain is thought to arise from extravascular bubbles pressing on nerves in the tendons and ligaments. The joints most often involved are the shoulders, elbows, knees, hips, and hands. Many victims of DCS describe this pain as an initial feeling of numbness in the joint or surrounding muscle. Over a short period of time, this often progresses to a deep, dull ache. Some victims also describe both a throbbing and sharp stabbing pain. Limb pain, researchers believe, arises from ischemia or increased pressure inside the bone. The pain usually continues for 12 to 24 hours, but can last for days.

Pain, however, is not necessarily a reliable indicator of the type of DCS a diver has, and that's one of the reasons the old classification system was abandoned. For instance, bubbles can form in nerves of the spinal column, resulting in pain in areas served by these nerves. In this case, discomfort is usually felt in the back or abdomen and is described as "girdle pain." So while the pain symptoms may give the appearance of so-called "pain-only" DCS, it could actually indicate neurological involvement.

Some cases of DCS involve what's known as simple "skin bends," in which bubbles block peripheral circulation, sometimes causing a measles-like rash. It's usually accompanied by severe itching. The symptoms often subside as the gas diffuses through the skin. To assist the outgassing process, the victim should breathe pure oxygen. If the symptoms subside in about a half hour, it's considered a mild form of DCS and does not require recompression therapy.

This condition should not, however, be confused with the more serious form of skin bends that is accompanied by a deep red to purple marbling, usually along the back or upper body. This is a very serious form of DCS—called cutaneous decompression sickness—and is usually a precursor to neurologic involvement. Luckily, this is uncommon among recreational divers.

According to statistics compiled by DAN, about two-thirds of all recreational divers who get DCS have some form of neurological involvement. This often results from bubble formation in the spinal cord. Specifically, it's theorized that bubbles form in the fatty tissues that surround the nerves. These bubbles then restrict blood flow to the nerves, or press directly on the nerves. This problem is compounded by the "bottleneck effect" described earlier. The unusual anatomy of the veins that service the spinal cord make it particularly prone to damage of this nature.

The symptoms of spinal DCS are numbness, tingling, or inability to move a limb. In severe cases, paralysis occurs—particularly of the lower body. Impairment or loss of either bladder or bowel control is also a relatively common symptom in severe cases. Deeper dives are especially prone to causing DCS with spinal cord involvement.

Pulmonary DCS—also known as "the chokes"—is extremely rare in recreational diving. It results from massive amounts of bubbles returning to the lungs in the venous circulation. The bubbles, in turn, cause congestion, blocking the efficient flow of blood through the lung capillary bed. This significantly impairs oxygen intake. The impaired circulation further reduces the elimination of nitrogen from the tissues. The result is the formation of still more bubbles. Common symptoms of this condition are: coughing, difficulty in breathing, and a feeling of tightness across the chest. Smoking can further aggravate the condition.

Yet another form of DCS occurs in the inner ear or vestibular organs. In the old U.S. Navy colloquial terminology, this was called "the staggers" due to the nature of the symptoms it caused. As the vestibular organs of the inner ear control our sense of balance, bubble formation in these organs can cause severe vertigo, nausea, ringing of the ears and even hearing loss. This form of DCS is rare in recreational divers.

Cerebral DCS or "brain bends" can occur for several reasons. Initially, researchers assumed it was caused primarily by bubbles forming in brain tissues. Because of its high perfusion, it was thought that the brain wasn't especially susceptible to DCS. Unfortunately, experience among recreational divers shows that brain bends is relatively common, often accompanying cases of supposed "pain only" DCS.

Even more startling is that cerebral involvement is often seen in cases of DCS where divers have not exceeded the no-decompression limits. These experiences lead researchers to conclude that cerebral DCS isn't usually caused by bubbles forming directly in brain tissue. Instead, they theorize, bubbles actually form elsewhere in the body and somehow make their way to the brain via the arterial blood flow.

But if bubbles make it to the brain, that means they must somehow bypass or otherwise get through the filtration process of the lungs. Exactly how these bubbles bypass the lungs is still debated by researchers, although several mechanisms have been proposed.

One way the bubbles may reach the brain involves the anatomy of the lungs. The theory states that when bubbles in the capillary beds build to excessive levels, vessels can open up, allowing some blood to bypass the affected region. This bypass mechanism is called *shunting*. Any bubbles present in the blood shunted around the alveoli now enter arterial circulation and can easily migrate to the brain.

Another theory on how bubbles bypass the lungs has great implications for repetitive diving. The theory goes like this: On an initial dive, significant silent bubbles develop and migrate to the capillary bed of the lungs. Because they are trapped there, they cause no problems. If the diver remains out of the water, the gases from the bubbles simply diffuse into the lungs. But if the diver makes a repetitive dive, the bubbles are compressed—possibly to the size where they can get through the capillaries and into the arterial circulation. This theory suggests a powerful rationale to avoid deep, short-duration repetitive dives, sometimes called "bounce dives."

A Hole in the Heart

A more recent explanation of how bubbles bypass the lungs involves a structure called the *patent foramen ovale* (PFO). To understand what a PFO is, and how it affects divers, we must review some basic anatomy

FIGURE 1-5

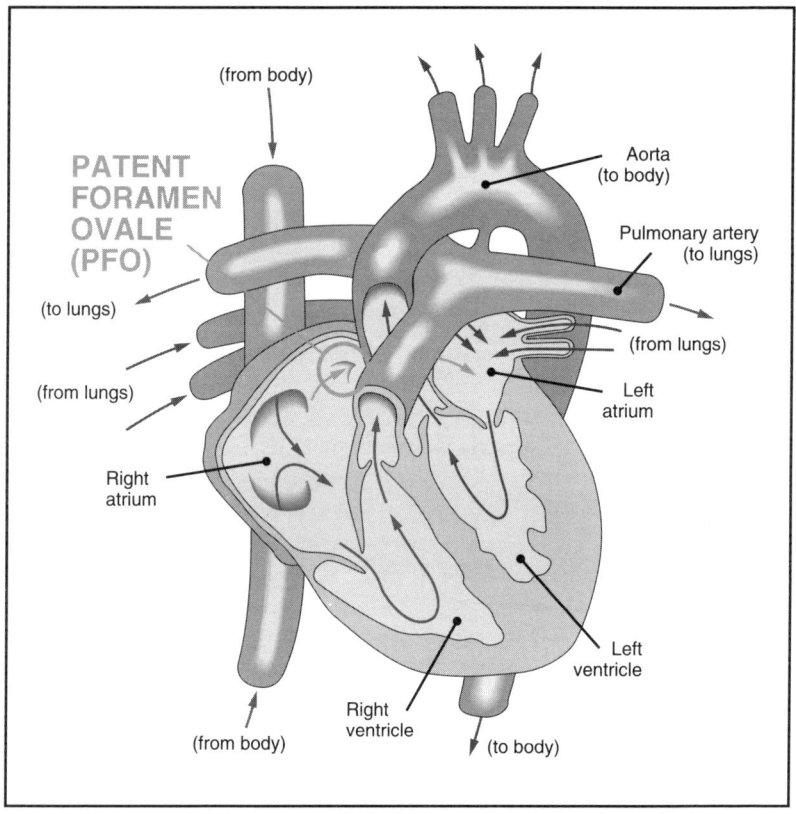

Location of a patent foramen ovale (PFO).

and human development. While in the womb, a fetus has no use for its lungs. It receives oxygen directly from the mother's blood supply. Thus, in fetal circulation, blood bypasses the lungs. One way this bypass occurs is by shunting the blood entering the right atrium directly into the left atrium through an opening called the foramen ovale. The foramen ovale is similar to a one-way "flapper valve."

At birth, when the newborn takes its first breath, the pressure in the left atrium increases and causes the flapper valve to close. Over time the valve normally seals shut. In perhaps as many as 25 to 30 percent of the population, however, the valve remains partially open (the medical term is *patent*). This allows small amounts of blood from the right atrium to seep into the left atrium. Under normal circumstances, this condition is of no consequence because the pressure in the left atrium is higher than the right. This tends to keep the valve closed.

This is of concern to our discussion of DCS because silent bubbles that develop in the venous circulation eventually make their way back to the heart. Under normal conditions, these bubbles are trapped by the minute blood vessels of the lungs. The trapped bubbles defuse into the lungs, and the gas is expired in the normal respiratory process.

Under some circumstances—when you equalize your ears, for example—the pressure in the right atrium can increase slightly over the left atrium. If a PFO is present, then blood can shunt from the right to left heart. This provides a pathway for not only small amounts of venous blood to bypass the lungs, but the silent bubbles contained in the blood as well.

Once in the left atrium, these microbubbles go directly into arterial circulation. Several studies have documented this phenomenon. Yet, as research is still limited on this subject, it's impossible to draw any solid conclusions about the implications of PFO. Nonetheless, while the PFO does not cause decompression sickness, additional bubbles entering the arterial blood flow in this manner may hasten the onset of symptoms or cause more severe forms of DCS. It could perhaps even cause arterial gas embolism.

One intriguing study comes from England where a researcher examined more than 100 cases of DCS. Of the test subjects who experienced symptoms of DCS within 30 minutes of surfacing, 66 percent had a PFO. In subjects experiencing symptoms later than 30 minutes, only 26 percent had a PFO. These data suggest a PFO may contribute to the early onset and severity of DCS.

Researchers caution against drawing any conclusions about the implications of PFO in divers as the phenomenon requires far more study. While certainly far from conclusive, the PFO issue provides yet another reason why we should dive conservatively. It also offers one more example of how much science has yet to learn about DCS.

DCS vs. DCI

These new theories of how DCS occurs have caused scientists to revise even the terminology they use to describe many diving disorders.

As you may remember from your training, bubbles that block arterial blood flow usually result from lung over-pressurization—a lung rupture. In some cases, however, gas bubbles are forced directly through the over-stretched alveolar membrane, resulting in no physical damage to the lungs. But regardless of origin, these are air bubbles rather than nitrogen. When a structure such as a blood clot blocks the flow of blood, it's called an *embolus*. When the blockage is caused by an air bubble, the condition is known as air embolism. (The more precise medical term is *arterial gas embolism* or simply AGE.) But what about the nitrogen bubbles that bypass the lungs and get into arterial circulation? They, too, can act as emboli, but they are not air bubbles and they weren't caused by lung over-pressurization.

To avoid confusion over the exact origin and mechanism of damage caused by bubble formation, scientists and physicians have begun using a new term. Today, instead of trying to distinguish between decompression sickness (DCS) and arterial gas embolism (AGE), medical authorities now use the all-encompassing term decompression illness (DCI). This describes any form of medical disorder resulting from decompression regardless of the mechanism involved—mechanical rupture or supersaturation.

Where Do We Go From Here?

Throughout this chapter, you probably noticed the continual use of terms like "thought to," "theorize," "generally believed," or "maybe." If this has lead you to the conclusion that science really understands for certain very little about DCS, then you're absolutely right. While we've known some basic facts about this unusual disorder for more than 100 years, we have much to learn.

CHAPTER TWO

If You Want a Guarantee, Buy a Washing Machine

An In-depth Look at Dive Tables

Decompression sickness is caused by staying at depth too long. But just what is "too long"? Divers and researchers have wrestled with this question for nearly a century, and yet they still can't answer it with any certainty.

The best estimates on how long is too long are called *dive tables*. But they do not guarantee that you can avoid the bends, so it's important to have an insight into how dive tables came into being and what limitations they have in predicting DCS.

Until recently, dive tables had only one meaning: the U.S. Navy Standard Air Decompression Tables. Until the late 1980s the USN Tables—or some version reformatted for ease of use—were the only tables used by most recreational divers.

Today, the USN Tables are only one of many you are likely to encounter. The parade of new tables has caused many to ask serious and fundamental questions about matters that were considered indisputable only a short time ago. And as we shall see in the next chapter, the explosion in dive computer technology has complicated the situation even further.

This chapter begins with the earliest observations of decompression sickness to show how science first tried to explain this mysterious disorder. Our discussion will then move on to the twentieth century and

PHOTO 2-1

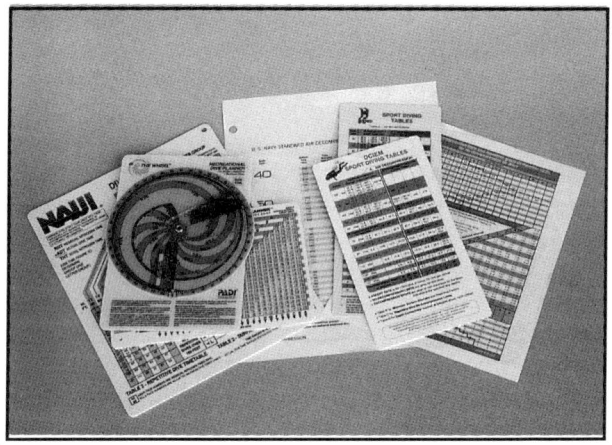

While the introduction of new tables has contributed to diving safety, the wide variation in their approaches to decompression planning can be confusing.

how the indomitable Professor Haldane attempted not only to explain, but also to prevent DCS. Next, we'll examine how the U.S. Navy refined much of Haldane's work to produce what by the 1950s became the standard not only for military diving operations, but for recreational divers as well.

The Haldanean approach, however, is not the only method of designing dive tables. If you are to have an in-depth understanding of the subject, you should have at least some knowledge of non-Haldanean methods. So, the concluding portion of this chapter explores tables and design methods slightly to vastly different than those used by Haldane and his advocates.

IN THE BEGINNING

Our story begins in England, in the year 1670, with a scientist named Sir Robert Boyle (the same guy, incidentally, responsible for "Boyle's Law"). A German by the name of Von Guericke had just invented the first vacuum pump. Boyle, who was fascinated with the behavior of gases, decided to build one himself. Using his newly constructed pump, he studied what would happen to various living organisms when they were placed in the vacuum chamber (or as he called it, an "exhausted receiver").

One of the first unfortunate victims to be "vacuumized" was a snake. Writing about his observations Boyle remarked, "I observed the viper furiously tortured in our exhausted receiver, which had manifestly a conspicuous bubble moving to and fro in the waterous humor of one of its eyes." This was the first recorded account of the phenomenon we now know as decompression sickness. The fate of the snake was not recorded.

There not being any great need to understand why bubbles form in the eyes of snakes, nothing more of consequence happened in the study of decompression until much later. Our story now moves ahead to the Industrial Revolution.

What powered the Industrial Revolution was, of course, the steam engine; and coal powered the steam engine. Thus, coal mining became an extremely important endeavor. As coal reserves were extracted near the surface, miners had to dig deeper. Unfortunately, the one limiting factor in digging mines deeper into the ground is that they eventually flood.

One way to prevent the flooding is to seal off and pressurize the mine. The increased ambient pressure keeps the water from flowing into the mine. Although the English claim to have been the first to have thought of it, a French engineer by the name of Triger was the first to accomplish this feat. He sunk the world's first pressurized mine in Chalons, France, in 1841.

While this new technology solved the flooding problem, it created a new one. Miners who were subjected to high pressure began turning up with a curious medical disorder. Triger and his associates noted the afflicted miners showed symptoms of "pain in the ears, a nasal quality of speech, and joint pains." His advice was to "rub the affected area with spirits of wine." What Triger did not know, but what is painfully obvious to any diver of today, was that his miners were bent.

The first scientific study of this new affliction was done by two French physicians, Pol and Wattelle. In 1854 they described the curious nature of the disorder citing, "The danger does not lie in entering a shaft containing compressed-air; nor in remaining there a longer or shorter time; decompression alone is dangerous." They realized the problem was a result of subjecting a person to increased pressure and then reducing that pressure. In 1857, another researcher named Hoppe concluded, based on autopsies of both animals and humans, that bubbles were responsible for the mysterious disorder. He deduced that the bubbles formed when gas was liberated too quickly from blood and tissue by excessive decompression. To reduce the likelihood of the disease, he suggested slowing the decompression rate.

In addition to mining, Triger's method was used in underwater construction. By building a pressurized chamber called a *caisson* to keep water out, men could work on the sea bed to build bridge foundations, tunnels, and other large-scale structures. His method soon gained wide application.

Caissons were first used in the U.S. to build bridges in 1869—initially a railroad bridge over the Pee Dee River in South Carolina. That same year a more ambitious project bridging the Mississippi River at St. Louis was begun. In this project, caisson workers were subjected to a record pressure of 80 psia (equivalent to almost 147 feet of sea water). Tragically, this project resulted in 35 cases of serious neurological DCS, including six fatalities. This is why, then, what we today call decompression sickness was first termed "caisson disease."

FIGURE 2-1

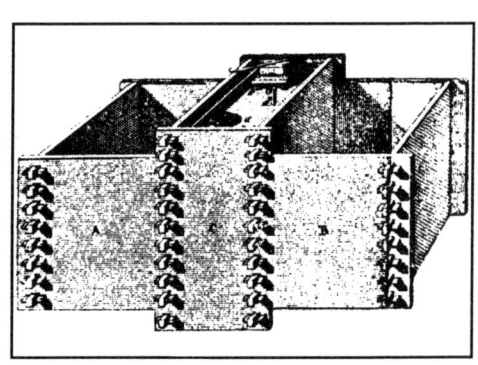

An example of nineteenth-century high technology: A caisson, like the one illustrated here, was floated into place and then lowered to the seabed by flooding portions of it. Caisson is a French word that literally means "big box."

As there was still little understanding of caisson disease, there was certainly no consensus on how to treat it. As early as the 1870s Andrew Smith, chief surgeon of the New York Bridge Company, suggested recompression as a treatment. Although he recommended this treatment during the construction of the Brooklyn Bridge, his advice was not heeded.

Meanwhile, back in France some important scientific work exploring decompression sickness was going on. In 1872 Paul Bert, a nineteenth-century Renaissance man—physiologist, physician, lawyer, and noted champion of women's rights—analyzed the gas bubbles in decompression experiments and found them to contain primarily nitrogen. He, like Hoppe, concluded the bubbles were indeed the cause of the bends. In 1879 he clinically described his theory in his landmark book *La Pression Barometrique*. This 1,800-page treatise was so significant and authoritative that it is still in print and cited today in medical literature on decompression sickness. He, too, recommended that caisson workers be brought back to surface pressure slowly, allowing nitrogen gas to escape before it was able to form bubbles.

Bert's major contribution was his recommendation for treating decompression sickness. He, like Andrew Smith, suggested the victims be recompressed, then slowly returned to surface pressure. But unlike any of his predecessors, he deduced that, because the bubbles were comprised mainly of nitrogen, victims would benefit from breathing pure oxygen to help flush the nitrogen from the body. (Sound familiar?) As a result of this recommendation, Bert was also the first person to discover that oxygen was toxic when breathed under too much pressure. In fact, the classic sign of oxygen toxicity—convulsions—has been given the formal name the "Paul Bert effect."

Bert's techniques were employed in 1893 during the construction of the tunnel connecting New York with Jersey City. The results were a marked decrease in the number of decompression sickness cases and reduction in the number of fatalities from the disorder. Yet, Bert's technique did not prevent all cases of DCS. There was still a need for a more definitive approach— a schedule that could provide a specific guideline for decompression.

By the end of the nineteenth century, diving technology had advanced beyond science's understanding of DCS. Depth limits were based more on avoiding bends than what was technically possible.

A Scot Named Haldane

As the twentieth century began, diving systems were improving, as were other innovations in underwater construction. Also becoming apparent was modern warfare's need for undersea technology. The gap was widening, however, between what was possible technologically versus physiologically. By the turn of the century, improvements in equipment enabled divers to reach depths of more than 200 feet. But, due to the effects of decompression sickness, the practical limit for diving was only about 120 feet [Figure 2-2].

In 1905 the British Royal Navy took the first step in what would become the birth of modern decompression technology. It commissioned a renowned Scottish physiologist, John Scott Haldane, to explore the problem of decompression. Haldane was a member of the Royal Navy's Admiralty Deep Water Diving Committee and had conducted research on improving the ventilation of diving helmets, so he was already familiar with diving operations. Now, his challenge was to provide a systematic method to decompress divers safely. In the end, not only did he succeed, but he extended the operational diving range to almost twice what was believed possible—210 feet!

The methods used to solve the problem of decompression are of interest for two reasons. First, they provide an important historical perspective. Second, and more importantly, the concepts and procedures Haldane devised are still used in designing dive tables today. It's impossible to have a full appreciation of dive tables without understanding Haldane's methodology.

Drawing on the work of Bert and others, Haldane understood that the formation of nitrogen bubbles was probably the cause of decompression sickness. These bubbles formed when, upon ascent, the pressure of nitrogen in the body was significantly greater than the pressure of the air the diver was breathing. As not all divers or caisson workers got the bends, he deduced that a person could tolerate a certain degree of excess nitrogen pressure without bubble formation. The problem was determining exactly what the "certain" amount was, and how the pressure could be reduced in a predictable way to avoid bubble formation.

As a good scientist, Haldane first wanted to observe the phenomenon he was studying to form a working hypothesis. From his observations of diving operations in a construction project in Gibraltar Harbor, he already knew that divers could safely dive for long periods of time in shallow water without getting DCS. But he now needed a more controlled way of studying the phenomenon. Fortunately, he had access to one of the only experimental hyperbaric chambers in existence—a boiler that had been converted for this purpose by Dr. Ludwig Mond.

Haldane realized that the preliminary tests would be too uncertain and potentially dangerous to use human subjects. The first problem, then, was determining which animal subject would be appropriate. He found that mice, rats, rabbits, and guinea pigs were extremely difficult to bend. Mice, for example, could be taken to a depth of 168 feet for more than an hour and brought back to the surface in less than a minute! (By contrast, we now know this dive would require more than 150 minutes of decompression for a human). There was yet another problem with these smaller animals—how do you know when they are bent? Signs of joint pain, for example, would be extremely difficult to detect in a rat or a guinea pig.

Finally, Haldane found a suitable animal model—the goat. Primarily because of their circulatory dynamics, goats more closely approximated humans than the smaller animals. They were more manageable in an experimental setting than primates. It was also easy to tell when they experienced pain by the way they lifted or favored the affected limb. Haldane's selection and use of goats has been borne out over the years. Even today they are used as test subjects in decompression studies.

Based on these experiments, Haldane noted a constant relationship: Decompression sickness did not occur as long as the pressure within the subject's tissues did not exceed twice the ambient pressure. This is the origin of his famous "2:1 ratio." He noted, for example, that goats could be taken to two atmospheres and brought up immediately to one atmosphere. Similarly, they could be pressurized to six atmospheres and brought immediately up to three atmospheres. He postulated that a diver could be brought immediately up to any depth provided the 2:1 ratio was not violated. Once the 2:1 ratio was achieved, the remaining portion of the ascent must proceed much more slowly to allow for elimination of the excess nitrogen. This was the genesis of the idea for stage decompression.

Still, designing precise schedules was not as easy as determining a simple ratio. Other factors also had to be considered—for example, gas absorption and elimination are not constant for all parts of the body. As we saw in Chapter One, these rates vary for two reasons: 1) the amount of blood flow to the tissue (how quickly gas gets to and from the tissue); and 2) the density of the tissue (how quickly gas disperses throughout the cells). This means that some tissues absorb and eliminate gas very quickly, while others do so very slowly.

Haldane's solution was quite ingenious. He knew that while there are probably hundreds of actual rates of absorption and elimination, it was neither possible nor necessary to consider every one. Instead, an overall picture could be described by looking at certain representative tissues. This is the origin of the multitissue model of decompression, still the most common way of designing decompression tables.

Haldane's use of the term *tissue* has resulted in a common myth concerning his and other decompression models. Many divers assume that Haldane's tissue compartments correspond to real human tissues. This isn't the case. Haldane used his observations to construct a mathematical model. Thus, his *tissues* were merely mathematical values used in his equations to predict rates of absorption and elimination. Scientists today prefer to use the term *compartment* rather than tissue to avoid this misconception.

Another of Haldane's assumptions was that both the absorption and elimination of gas occurred at an exponential rate. To help you understand the concept, just crack the valve of a full scuba tank. If you can stand the noise, you'll see an exponential relationship in action. Once fully opened, the tank will purge half of its air very quickly. Then the air flow will slow down progressively, with the last few hundred psi taking quite some time to drain. This same relationship occurs when the tank is being filled—quickly at first, then a gradual slowing.

To describe exponential relationships Haldane turned to a common system of description used even today in nuclear science and pharmacology—a half-life or half-time. A half-time is simply the amount of time something (in this case a tissue compartment) takes to either fill or empty half of what it's assumed to hold (in this case nitrogen gas). It's then assumed that in six half-times the effect is complete.

For example, Haldane's model contained the half-times: 5, 10, 20, 40, and 75 minutes. Let's look at his fastest compartment—five minutes (see *Figure 2-3*). In the first five minutes the compartment will fill to 50 percent. In the next five minutes, it will fill half its remaining capacity (75 percent full). Five minutes more will take it halfway again for a total of 87.5 percent. After the fourth half-time it will be 93.6 percent full, and 96.9 percent after the fifth. Finally, after the six half-time or 30 minutes (6 x 5 = 30), the compartment is considered full at 98.4 percent. (Mathematically, it can never reach 100 percent.)

Haldane deduced that different compartments would reach their maximum levels according to the diver's depth (pressure) and bottom time (duration). He provided for the compartment that came closest to

FIGURE 2-3

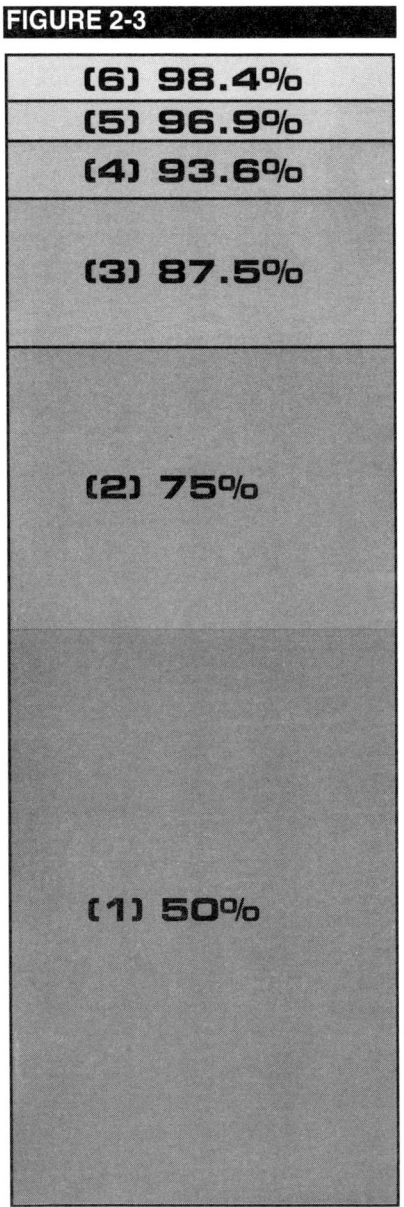

Half-times express exponential relationships—such as absorption of nitrogen.

the maximum allowable pressure to exercise "control" over the decompression requirement. The tedious and complex computations required to create the tables obviously involved many hundreds of hours.

With a method to calculate nitrogen pressures in any of his tissue compartments, Haldane could then determine the time and depth from which a diver could ascend without exceeding the maximum allowable nitrogen pressure in any compartment. If the diver exceeded the maximum tissue pressure, then a decompression stop was required. Halting the ascent at predetermined intervals allowed for reduction in the nitrogen pressure in the diver's tissues. Once the stop was completed, the tissue pressures were reduced and the diver could then ascend to the surface.

In 1908 Haldane and his associates, Boycott and Damant, published the results of their research in an article titled "The Prevention of Compressed Air Illness." Included was the first set of tables giving divers specific time and depth guidelines. This article is probably the single most important hallmark in the history of the dive tables. Virtually all dive tables used by recreational divers today were derived—with refinements—using the principles laid down by Haldane. As divers, we all owe him a great deal.

Although Haldane made an incalculable contribution to the field of decompression, his system was far from perfect. In actual use, divers found his short duration table—dives of less than two hours—to be too conservative. Additionally, his long duration table—dives of more than two hours—did not provide for sufficient decompression.

In addition, Haldane's tables had no provision for "repetitive diving." At the time, all diving was surface-supplied and conducted for a specific purpose. There was no need to consider the consequences of a diver making a second dive after a brief surface interval. The diver simply remained underwater until the task was accomplished.

With the advent of mechanical air compressors, divers could go even deeper than with hand-operated pumps. Unfortunately, they discovered that Haldane's principles didn't work adequately at these more extreme depths.

To solve these shortcomings, the British Royal Navy undertook a project to extend Haldane's tables, allowing dives to 300 feet. Assigned to this task was Royal Navy Captain G.C.C. Damant—one of Haldane's research associates—and the diving company of Siebe Gorman & Co., Ltd. After additional animal experiments and actual test dives, they achieved their goal of greater depth by reducing Haldane's original 2:1 surfacing ratio to 1.75:1.

It would be left to others to refine Haldane's work even further and make dive tables safer and more reliable. And it would take the introduction of scuba to create a need for repetitive diving tables. Our story now takes us back across the Atlantic to work done by the U.S. Navy.

CONTRIBUTIONS OF THE U.S. NAVY

The first step in the U.S. Navy's contribution to dive tables began in 1912 when a Navy warrant officer and diver, George Stillson, submitted a report to the Naval Bureau of Construction and Repair. The report condemned the inadequate state of diving equipment and technique within the U.S. Navy. (The vast majority of diving at that time did not exceed 60 feet.) Aware of the advances made by the Royal Navy, Stillson suggested the U.S. Navy look at adapting a similar approach to decompression diving.

Acting on Stillson's recommendation, the Navy began a series of tests to evaluate Captain Damant's expanded tables. The tests took

PHOTO 2-2

The salvage of the sunken F-4 submarine in 1915 still holds the record for the deepest salvage operation ever undertaken using standard deep-sea diving dress on compressed air.

place in 1913 at the new Navy Experimental Diving Station (later to become the Experimental Diving Unit) at the Naval Ship Yard in Brooklyn, New York, and aboard the support vessel *USS Walkie.* Eventually, more than 300 test dives were conducted at depths of up to 270 feet. The Navy refined Damant's tables primarily by having the diver breathe pure oxygen during decompression. Based on this research, the first Navy tables were published in 1915 and became known as the Bureau of Construction and Repair Tables.

The first practical application of the Navy's deep diving tests came quickly. In 1915 the Navy submarine *F-4* sunk in Amala Bay off Honolulu in 300 feet of water. It was the first boat lost in the Navy's 15 years in submarine operations. Twenty-one men lost their lives. The Navy wanted to recover both the victims and the vessel. The first dive of the salvage operation fell to a small, 127-pound Navy diver, Frank Crilley. Using the new tables, Crilley safely returned from the world-record depth of 306 feet. To this day, recovery of the *F-4* holds the record for the deepest salvage operation ever undertaken using standard deep-sea diving dress on compressed air.

Stillson's tests and the F-4 salvage operation resulted in the Navy establishing the first deep sea diving school at the U.S. Naval Torpedo Station in Newport, Rhode Island, in 1916. In 1924 the Navy published its first diving manual. The foundation was now in place for the Navy to assume a leading role in decompression theory and table development.

The next important development came about in the early 1930s when researcher Charles Shilling, using volunteers, organized a series of experimental dives and showed that no existing model could adequately predict decompression for prolonged deep dives. In 1935, by analyzing Shilling's data, another researcher, J.A. Hawkins, drew an important conclusion: Haldane was wrong. In his model, Haldane had assumed that the 2:1 surfacing ratio was consistent for all tissue compartments. Hawkins concluded this wasn't the case. Rather than a single ratio, each compartment should have its own surfacing ratio.

In 1937 O.D. Yarbrough expanded upon Hawkins' work. He concluded that the five- and ten-minute compartments could tolerate such a large reduction in pressure that they could be ignored. Accounting for increased gas loading due to exercise, however, Hawkins' ratios for the remaining compartments were reduced even further than previous recommendations.

Based on Yarbrough's conclusions, the Navy published a revised set of tables that same year. Eliminating the fast 5- and 10-minute compartments, Yarbrough's tables included only the 20, 40, and 75-minute compartments. Each compartment was given an individual surfacing ratio. This version of the Navy tables soon gained acceptance around the world and represented the most significant advance in table design since Haldane's original work.

Although an important step forward, Yarbrough's tables—like Haldane's—weren't perfect. They were still unable to handle decompression requirements for prolonged deep dives. As World War II approached, however, the Navy's priorities shifted to other matters. Yarbrough's tables remained in use by Navy divers through the war.

Scuba and the Post-War Era

After the war the Navy resumed its work on refining the dive tables. O.E. Van Der Aue was exploring ways to enable surface decompression, a procedure in which the diver ascends to the surface—either immediately or after an abbreviated decompression stop—then is rapidly transferred to a recompression chamber to complete the decompression requirement.

During his tests, Van Der Aue found that Yarbrough's tables were completely inadequate in many circumstances. For example, in one test to 100 feet for 85 minutes half of his volunteer subjects got decompression sickness.

By the early 1950s the Navy concluded it should revise its tables to improve their safety and reliability. Of the staff of researchers assigned the task of refining the tables, two are particularly notable—M. Des Granges and J.V. Dwyer. From their research they concluded that as the depth and time of a dive increase, so must the depth of the decompression stop. They also restored to the decompression model the fast five- and ten-minute compartments.

They also added a much longer half-time compartment—120 minutes. (The slowest compartment for both the Haldane and Yarbrough models was 75 minutes.) This was done to account for long duration, deep dives—the major flaw in previous tables. Later, Robert Workman developed an Exceptional Exposure Table using even slower tissue half-times of 160, 200, and 240 minutes.

PHOTO 2-3

The introduction of scuba to the Navy diving program after World War II fostered the need to consider the diver's decompression status after multiple dives. Until then, dive tables did not account for repetitive diving.

While these revisions were necessary to increase the safety of decompression diving, another consideration influenced the decision to revise the tables—scuba. Scuba presented a novel problem to table designers: how to deal with a limited air supply. This had never been a problem before because all diving had been surface-supplied. With a virtually unlimited air supply, divers could always remain at depth until their tasks were completed. With scuba, however, the limited supply of air in the tank would at times require the diver to surface to change tanks. Thus was born the need for repetitive diving.

The need to exit and reenter the water presented a unique problem. It required Des Granges and Dwyer to come up with a way of accounting for the amount of excess nitrogen held over in the diver's tissues after surfacing. This extra quantity of nitrogen, termed residual nitrogen, was expressed using another new concept—the Repetitive Group Designation or "pressure group."

Second, they had to calculate how much residual nitrogen would leave a diver's tissues while on the surface. Solving this problem resulted in an entirely new component of the dive tables—the Surface Credit Interval Table. Using the 120-minute tissue compartment—the slowest tissue in their model—the new table allowed divers to calculate how much nitrogen was eliminated in the time interval between dives. This nitrogen status could then be taken into consideration before reentering the water for later dives.

In 1958 the revised U.S. Navy Standard Air Decompression Tables were published. Immediately adopted by the fledgling recreational diving community in America, these tables became the standard for decompression procedures. This standard remained with us until the recent proliferation of new dive tables and computers.

M-Values and Human Errors

Seeking to make the process of computing decompression schedules less complex, Robert Workman introduced the concept of M-values (short for "maximum values") in 1965. Up until this time, decompression status was calculated based on Haldane's method of comparing various "surfacing ratios." This was a complex and mathematically tedious process.

Workman's idea was to define the maximum amount of nitrogen allowed within any compartment not as a ratio, but as an expression of pressure. Specifically, pressure in feet of sea water (fsw). For example, let's look at the nitrogen pressure in our tissues here at the surface using his method. First, Workman reasoned that another way of expressing the pressure of one atmosphere is to say it's equivalent to 33 fsw. Thus, the terms 1 ATA, 14.7 psi, or 33 fsw are all the same expression of pressure. As our atmosphere is made up of about 78 percent nitrogen, we can say that, at the surface, our tissues contain a nitrogen pressure of 26 fsw (33 fsw x 78% = 25.74 fsw.) With his system Workman was able to simplify the computation process.

Another advantage of Workman's method becomes clear by looking at how he handled one of the tissue compartments. In the Navy model the surfacing ratio for the five-minute tissue compartment is 3.15 atmospheres to 1. This means the compartment is allowed to hold 3.15 times the surface pressure before a decompression stop is required.

FIGURE 2-4

Tissue half-time	Total pressure surfacing ratio	Nitrogen pressure surfacing ratio	Surfacing M-Value
5 minutes	4.00:1	3.15:1	104 FSW
10 minutes	3.40:1	2.67:1	88 FSW
20 minutes	2.75:1	2.18:1	72 FSW
40 minutes	2.22:11	1.76:1	58 FSW
80 minutes	2.00:1	1.58:1	52 FSW
120 minutes	1.96:1	1.55:1	51 FSW

Instead of a ratio, however, Workman expressed this maximum value as 104 fsw. (The surface value of 33 fsw x 3.15 = 103.95 fsw.) As each tissue had its own surfacing ratio under the old ratio system, Workman's system assigned each tissue its own individual M-value. This method of computing decompression status was far simpler than continually comparing ratios. In fact, it is still used in virtually all popular decompression models even today. The various surfacing ratios and M-values used in the Navy model are listed in *Figure 2-4*.

While most recreational divers adopted the U.S. Navy Tables without question or reservation, they originally contained numerous errors. Commander Ed Thalmann of the Navy Experimental Diving Unit discovered the errors in 1983 when he recalculated the tables using a computer. In the mid-1950s when the Navy Dive Tables were developed, computers were rare, and computer time was expensive. As a result, the tables were originally derived mostly by tedious hand calculation. Not surprisingly, given the thousands of computations required to produce the tables, human error entered the picture. And not only were mistakes made in computation, but transcription errors occurred when the data were put into tabular form and published.

Most of the computation errors in the tables occurred in the Surface Credit Interval Table, while the transcription errors were on the No-Decompression Table. Fortunately, the air supply limitations of scuba prevented these errors from affecting recreational diving. The errors, therefore, had little or no practical effect on recreational scuba divers.

In the final analysis, regardless of the problems, errors, or inconsistencies with the U.S. Navy Tables, they served the recreational diving community well for nearly 30 years. Considering they were never intended for use by civilian divers, the incalculable number of safe hours of bottom time these tables have provided is testament to the good science that went into their development. We owe a great deal to the U.S. Navy in helping to make recreational diving a safe activity.

NEW FRONTIERS AND BEYOND

Nearly a century has passed since Professor Haldane and his associates published the first dive tables. In that same time we have progressed from the Wright Brothers to the space shuttle. We have gone from Alexander Graham Bell to bouncing microwaves off of orbiting satellites. But the technology of dive tables has not kept the same pace. Only in the past few decades have researchers even begun exploring how to develop dive tables in fundamentally new ways.

Decompression theories have been no stranger to debate and inquiry. Yet, only since the birth of recreational diving have serious challenges been made to Haldane's view of decompression.

Also recently called into question have been many of the assumptions used in developing the U.S. Navy Dive Tables. What we believed to be absolute truth when many of us began our careers as divers has been cast aside or, at the least, hotly debated. The only certainty about dive tables anymore is that we have taken but a few steps in a long journey. One day we may have a proven and thoroughly understood method of avoiding decompression sickness, but that day is still far in the future.

Bubbles, Bubbles Everywhere

One of the first challenges to Haldane's theory of decompression centered around the way gas bubbles form. Haldane believed bubble formation was essentially spontaneous, occurring soon after a tissue's saturation limit was exceeded. Much like being pregnant, one was either bent or wasn't. The scientific term is *homogeneous nucleation.*

As early as 1942 this concept was challenged by U.S. Naval researcher Albert Behnke. One of the great names in the field of diving physiology, Behnke deduced that small harmless bubbles probably formed before reaching a size that caused DCS. As we saw in the last chapter, these are called *asymptomatic* or *"silent bubbles."*

The implication of this silent-bubble theory was that bubble formation was not, as Haldane assumed, spontaneous. Instead, bubbles

PHOTO 2-4

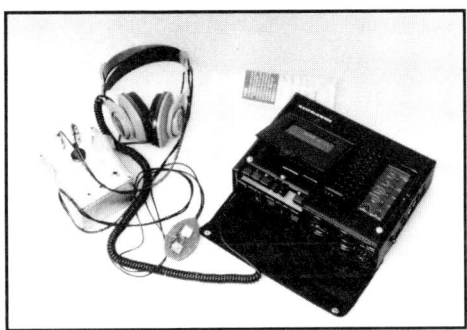

A Doppler Bubble Detector—Although its value is disputed by some, it's nonetheless the most popular way of testing dive tables.

formed gradually, developing first from tiny gas micronuclei. As opposed to Haldane's theory of homogeneous nucleation, this is called *heterogeneous nucleation.* Still, as there were no technological means to confirm the hypothesis in Behnke's time, it was all just theory.

By the late 1950s advances in technology were occurring that would confirm the silent bubbles hypothesis. Two researchers, Satomura and Franklin, had begun to use ultrasonic (extreme high frequency sound) waves to monitor blood flow and heart function. They used was a Doppler Ultrasonic Flowmeter. In 1968 Merrill Spencer and S.D. Campbell were the first to detect gas bubbles in the circulation of sheep decompressed from 200 feet for an hour. The technology was first used to detect silent bubbles in humans in 1969.

As Doppler ultrasonic technology was able to detect bubbles before the onset of decompression sickness, researchers believed they had a more refined way to test the safety of dive tables. (In the Navy's research to develop its decompression tables, the test criterion was whether the diver did or did not get the bends.) The idea was that silent bubbles could be used as a predictor of more serious bubble formation elsewhere in the body. Furthermore, tables could be designed to keep silent bubbling to a minimum. (See next page for a more detailed look at Doppler technology).

Although this theory is the most widely used means of testing dive tables today, it is nonetheless unproved. No clear correlation has been established between silent bubbles and their relationship to DCS.

Regardless of the uncertainty of the relationship of silent bubbling to decompression sickness, the 1970s saw several landmark Doppler studies of the U.S. Navy Tables. Virtually all researchers found the same result: Significant silent bubbling occurred in divers well before the maximum limits of the tables were reached. To minimize silent

What Doppler Detectors Can Do...

A Doppler Bubble Detector is basically an adaptation of the Doppler Ultrasound Flowmeter, developed in the 1960s to monitor blood flow. It's an acoustical device based on a phenomenon in physics known as the Doppler effect or Doppler shift (named for an Austrian scientist, Christian Johann Doppler, who discovered the effect in 1842).

This phenomenon applies to all types of waves, including light and sound. It's important to astronomers and astrophysicists who study the universe. In terms of its application to sound, the classic example of a Doppler shift is the rise and fall of the pitch of a locomotive's whistle as it approaches and moves away from a stationary listener. It also occurs when the listener approaches or recedes from a stationary sound.

The Doppler effect occurs when a sound source approaches the listener. The waves in front of the source are squeezed together so the listener receives a larger number of waves than would have been received from a stationary source over the same time. This causes a rise in pitch. When the sound source moves away, the waves spread farther apart, and the listener receives fewer waves per unit of time, resulting in a lower pitch.

The Doppler Detector works by sending ultrasonic waves into the diver's body. These waves reflect back to the monitor, making a distinctive sound according to the density of whatever they encounter. The telltale snaps, whistles, pops or chirps indicate moving bubbles. (This is the same technology used to image a fetus in the womb.)

This technology prompts some to ask why we can't avoid the bends by taking such a device with us under water. Unfortunately, the technology doesn't give us a way of directly preventing DCS for several reasons. First, most silent or asymptomatic bubbling doesn't occur until the diver has surfaced, so monitoring under water would not do us much good. But even more important is that the bubbles detected are those in

bubble formation, many researchers, such as Merrill Spencer, Bruce Bassett, and Andrew Pilmanis, published revised no-decompression limits. They also advocated other conservative practices, such as safety stops before ascending.

New Technology Means New Tables

In 1981 one of the first "new tables" appeared. A bioengineer then at the University of Michigan—Karl Huggins—produced the "No-Bubble Table." Using procedures similar to those used to design the U.S. Navy the venous bloodstream, and under normal circumstances they're scrubbed by the lungs. In other words, the bubbles detected by the Doppler are not the bubbles that are generally believed to cause DCS. (As we saw in Chapter One, under certain unusual circumstances some of these bubbles can make their way into arterial circulation and cause big problems). What science thinks causes DCS are static bubbles throughout the body that impair circulation and press on nerves or distort tissues. Detecting symptomatic bubbles is beyond our current technological capability. Even a Doppler has its limitations; it can't, for example, detect a moving bubble if it's less than about one ten-thousandth of a centimeter.

You might ask, if it doesn't tell us anything useful, then why use a Doppler Detector at all? While a Doppler may not allow us literally "to listen to the bends," that doesn't mean the information it yields is useless. Many theorists hold that a correlation exists between the degree of silent bubbling and the onset of DCS. It's much like the old "canary in the coal mine" idea where an effect on one thing warns us before something else happens. The problem is that such a correlation between silent bubbling and DCS has never been clearly established. In fact, experience has shown that divers sometimes get bent even if they have a zero bubble grade (essentially, no bubbles). And sometimes divers have the highest possible grade but don't show any signs of DCS.

Another limitation of the Doppler Detector is that it allows monitoring of only the bloodstream, a mere 8 percent of the body. So, some say, how good of a picture does it really provide?

Still, even with all its limitations, the Doppler Detector is the only means we have of studying actual bubbles in the body. Until something more effective comes along, it's a whole lot better than knowing nothing about what's going on inside us.

---

tables, Huggins incorporated Spencer's Doppler-derived no-decompression limits. Although rare, this table can still be found in use today.

Up until this time the advances in table design came directly out of the hyperbaric scientific community. But, the situation was about to change. The next major event occurred based on the insights of a recreational diver, Dr. Raymond Rogers, who in 1983 published an article entitled "The Dive Tables: A Different View." In his article he pointed out that the Navy's decompression tables had certain limitations for recreational (no-decompression) divers. Like many before him, he reiterated that the Navy no-decompression limits might be too liberal. But that was far from a radical idea. More importantly, Rogers introduced recreational divers to a limitation of the Navy tables that no one else had noticed: For handling outgassing during surface intervals, the Navy Tables were probably more conservative then necessary.

The long surface interval times—up to 12 hours—of the U.S. Navy Tables are based on using the slow 120-minute tissue compartment to control outgassing. The Navy designed its tables for decompression diving; and after a decompression dive, a slow compartment might have to be considered in planning a repetitive dive.

Rogers' hypothesis was that if divers don't decompress—as in recreational diving—they could be freed from the hefty restrictions of slow outgassing during a surface interval. Rather than the 120-minute compartment, Rogers determined through computer analysis that a half-time as fast as 60 minutes could control outgassing during a surface interval.

This provocative theory sparked the interest of the Professional Association of Diving Instructors (PADI). Intrigued by Rogers' hypothesis, PADI established a company—Diving Science and Technology Corporation (DSAT)—to fund a scientific assessment. Over the next four years, under the leadership of noted hyperbaric researcher Dr. Michael

PHOTO 2-5

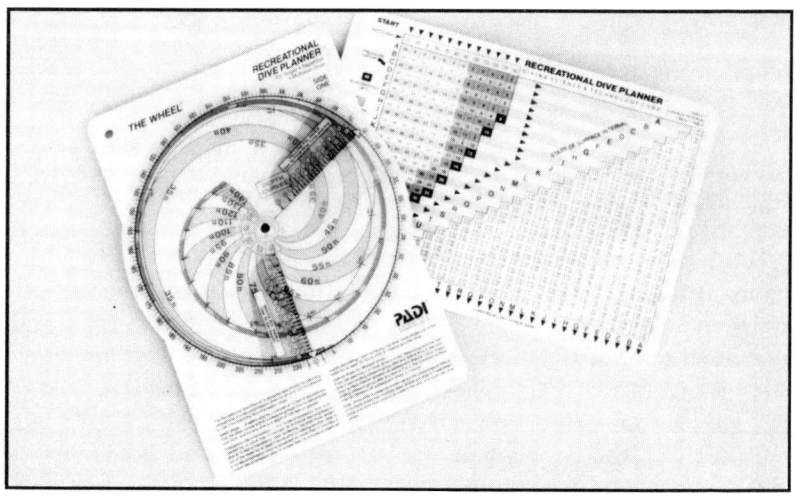

DSAT's Recreational Dive Planner or RDP—both table and wheel version—represent the first dive tables designed exclusively for recreational diving.

Powell, Rogers' theory was confirmed. No cases of DCS occurred in nearly 1,400 chamber and open-water test dives. In addition, fewer than 10 percent of the test subjects even demonstrated silent bubbles. The result was the creation in 1987 of the Recreational Dive Planner— the table now used in all PADI-sanctioned diver training courses.

Used throughout the world today, the Recreational Dive Planner has become one of the most popular dive tables in existence. Some dive computer manufacturers now base outgassing calculations in their devices on the Rogers/Powell research results; and another model using a completely Rogers-based algorithm will be released soon. For the recreational diver, the Recreational Dive Planner was an important advance in table design.

We Know How it Goes in...
But How Does it Come Out?

Another controversy concerning Haldane's theory centers around how gas is eliminated. Haldane assumed that both inert gas absorption and elimination occurred at the same exponential rate. This is referred to today by researchers as the E-E model. (E-E meaning exponential in, and exponential out). Thus, the rate at which the gas goes in is the same rate at which it comes out.

Some researchers dispute this assumption. Researcher and dive computer engineer Dr. John Lewis cites studies from the U.S. Navy. Tests from the Navy's Experimental Diving Unit conducted by Commander Ed Thalmann have shown that in certain circumstances the traditional view of gas absorption and elimination just doesn't work. It is particularly flawed when used to avoid bends on deeper repetitive dives with short surface intervals.

This has led some researchers to devise a new model: that while gas absorption is exponential, elimination occurs at a much slower, linear rate. Hence, the E-L model (for exponential in, linear out). This variance in decompression theory is likely to be an important issue in the future development of dive tables and computers.

CONTRA HALDANE

A more elemental criticism also is offered by the hyperbaric scientific community. Some in the field believe that Haldane was fundamentally wrong. They concede that Haldanean models have been good at helping recreational divers avoid decompression sickness, but they contend these models have no foundation in physiological reality. In essence, Haldane merely came up with a clever way of predicting decompression requirements.

Other researchers take a more moderate approach and say that Haldane's theory works only under certain circumstances; or that his theory explains only part of the picture. This situation shows that modern science actually knows very little for certain about the decompression phenomenon. Researchers in the field of decompression are far from unified in either their theories or methods. If Haldane's basic theories were incorrect, then we should explore some alternative approaches.

Oh, Canada!

In the early 1960s D. J. Kidd and R.A. Stubbs were doing some important work at the Defence Research Medical Laboratory and the Canadian Forces Institute of Aviation Medicine. Unsatisfied using a purely Haldanean/U.S. Navy model to solve the decompression dilemma, they decided to approach the problem in a different way.

In the Haldanean model, compartments are arranged in what can be termed a *parallel* sequence. Each compartment is assumed to be separate—having no interaction with any other compartment. Kidd and Stubbs concluded, however, that the tissues of our body don't act independently of one another. They developed the first decompression model that considered the interaction among compartments. As opposed to the Haldanean parallel model, this is called a *serial* model. Between 1962 and 1965 they succeeded in producing a successful dive computer based on this premise.

In 1971 Canada's Defence Research Medical Laboratory and the Institute of Environmental Medicine merged into the Defence and Civil Institute of Environmental Medicine (DCIEM), and continued research into decompression and dive computers. In 1977 DCIEM scientist Ken Kisman and a researcher from the French Navy, Gerard Masurel, developed the K-M bubble classification code for bubbles detected using Doppler ultrasound. This classification system is still used in most Doppler studies today.

DCIEM began a series of studies in 1979 using the Doppler ultrasonic bubble detection method to investigate the decompression stress imposed on divers using tables based on the Kidd-Stubbs model. For

PHOTO 2-6

Based on the extensively tested DCIEM decompression model, the DCIEM Sport Diving Tables were first released in 1988 and have since become widely accepted.

the next four years, an extensive series of Doppler experiments were conducted using this model as a reference.

In 1983 the Canadian Forces decided to construct its own set of dive tables (it had been using U.S. Navy tables). Under the direction of Lieutenant-Commander G.R. Lauckner and scientist Ron Nishi, DCIEM was given the task of developing these new tables. Based on the research conducted over the previous years and extensive computer simulations, a modified version of the Kidd-Stubbs model was produced known as the DCIEM 1983 decompression model. After several years of testing and validation in recompression chambers using both dry and wet divers in cold water conditions of 40-50 degrees F, the DCIEM Tables were released in 1985. Universal Dive Techtronics published a recreational diving version in 1988, followed by an expanded version in 1990 and a technical diving table for cave and research diving in 1994.

Today, the highly respected DCIEM tables represent a significant advance for diving safety. In addition to being adopted by a number of government and naval authorities throughout the world, they have been approved for use in certification courses sanctioned by the majority of diver training organizations in North America.

Tiny Bubbles...

Although the Kidd-Stubbs model differs from a pure Haldanean model in the arrangement of the compartments, the two have some similarities. That is, in a symptom-free diver the nitrogen within each compartment is assumed always to be in a dissolved state. Recent biomedical research, however disputes this assumption.

Microscopic bubbles exist in virtually every liquid or liquid-based substance on Earth—including human tissue. In addition, we now know that for various physiological reasons the human body has a proclivity for making gas seeds or microbubbles, even among those not involved in diving. This has given rise to a whole new approach to decompression theory sometimes called *free phase dynamics*, or more popularly the "tiny bubble model."

Advocates of free phase dynamics models contend that their approach offers hope of a more accurate biophysical model of inert gas absorption and elimination. Accordingly, they believe that dive tables derived from free phase models will be more reliable than tables based on a Haldanean-type model.

Researchers such as Drs. David Yount and Bruce Wienke have made strong arguments against the purely Haldanean view of decompression. Pointing especially to the difficulty Haldanean models have demonstrated in handling multiple-day repetitive diving, tiny bubble advocates seek a more complete picture. They have proposed decompression models that recognize that gas micronuclei will inevitably develop into bubbles during a dive. The key to the success of a decompression model is, therefore, to keep the quantity and size of these microbubbles below a critical limit.

Perhaps the most complete picture of decompression might be a merging of dissolved phase and free phase gas dynamics into a single theory. This idea is intriguing, and some believe it holds great promise.

The Magic of Mathematics and the New U.S. Navy Tables

Some theories are even outside the realm of either free phase or dissolved phase dynamics. One such model was developed by Captain Paul Weathersby, a researcher at the U.S. Naval Medical Research Institute (NMRI), and his associates, Shalini Survanshi and Eric Parker, in conjunction with Captain Ed Thalmann, former commander of the Navy's Experimental Diving Unit (EDU). Termed the Maximum Likelihood Model, Weathersby's hypothesis views decompression sickness as "probabilistic risk" dependent upon the depth and duration of the dive. This model, which ignores traditional issues such as how bubbles form, is based entirely on the science of probability and statistics.

Viewed another way, the theory says that if you know the outcome—bends or no bends—of certain dive profiles from actual experience, then you can use this information to create a probabilistic model and develop more successful dive tables. Naval researchers have made an extensive database of 2,300 well-documented dives compiled by the U.S. Navy, Royal Navy, and Canadian Forces. Using this data and appropriate statistical analysis, they have come up with models that enable them to construct dive tables with the "risk of bends" measured as a percentage. For example, a table could have a 1 percent, 5 percent—or whatever percentage risk factor is desired—according to the constraints incorporated into the equations.

The US Navy is expected to release a new set of tables based on the Maximum Likelihood Model. In general, no-decompression times in the 60- to 110-foot range will probably remain close to the current limits because the Navy believes it has enough experience in this area to validate the times. As NMRI has computed the DCS risk in this range as 2.3 percent, this figure was also used in calculating the revised no-decompression limits for other depths and for dives with total decompression time up to 20 minutes. Higher risk factors—from 5 to 10 percent—were selected for dives requiring longer decompression. This higher risk keeps the dive schedules practical for operational use.

The practical effect of all this is that no-decompression limits in the 60- to 110-foot range will stay about the same. But limits in shallower ranges will allow less time, with longer times allowed for deeper dives. According to the Navy, the overall DCS risk should be somewhat lower than that of the current tables.

A major difference between the Navy 's current tables and the new ones will be in format. Abandoning the familiar "repetitive group designation" approach, the new tables will have 26 "dive states," with a procedure for going from an exit state to an entry state. Also abandoned is the idea of "residual nitrogen time." Instead, divers will simply use one of 26 tables based on their entry state.

Probably the most important change is that under the new Navy system a table is defined as having either a greater or lesser chance of causing DCS. It abandons the idea of a table being safe or unsafe, which are terms with little meaning when it comes to decompression.

The Outer Limits and What We Really Know

Some highly experimental approaches to the decompression phenomenon almost seem to come out of science fiction. One such study undertaken by the U.S. Navy used a short-lived radioactive isotope of nitrogen as a way of actually tracing the gas as it was absorbed and eliminated. The rationale was that, rather than relying on any mathematical prediction models, the researchers could derive a truly "physiologically-based" theory by observing the behavior of nitrogen in the human body. This line of research has apparently been abandoned.

Centuries before Columbus, the native peoples of Central America developed a calendar that rivaled anything known in Europe. They had a highly accurate prediction model to plan the events of their lives. Their view of what forces drove the universe, however, were somewhat off-base. The sun moved across the sky, they believed, because it was carried in the talons of an eagle. As far as decompression theory goes, we may be in a state similar to our ancestors.

No one can dispute that the contributions of countless researchers have given us reasonably accurate prediction models to guide our decisions as recreational divers. Nonetheless, while we might descend and ascend with a fair assurance of safety, no one has yet unraveled the complete mystery of the decompression phenomenon. We, too, could be as far off-base in explaining decompression as the native Americans were at explaining the universe. Only time will tell. Just remember, while your new washing machine may come with a guarantee, don't expect one with your dive tables.

CHAPTER THREE

It Doesn't Matter What Tables You *Don't* Use

A Review of Dive-Table Procedures

While on a dive trip many years ago, I was buddied with a relatively new diver. As we were planning a dive to more than 100 feet of depth, I was concerned about how my novice friend would handle such a challenging experience. But to my relief, he turned out to be an extremely skilled and safety-conscious diver—or so I thought.

Back on board I congratulated him for his exemplary performance. Then, searching through my dive bag, I realized that my dive tables were gone. Eager to verify our decompression status, I asked my buddy, "What group are we in?"

He replied, "On this boat you don't have to dive in groups—as long as you have a buddy!"

I laughed, and explained that I meant what repetitive group we were in, not whether we had to dive in a group. I stopped laughing, however, when I heard his answer. "Repetitive group?" he said. "What's that?"

Puzzled at his seeming ignorance, all I could think to say was, "You know, your dive tables!"

While I was amused by his first response, it didn't prepare me for the shock of his second. As he explained, "Oh, I never understood how to use those things. Besides, I always let the divemaster figure that stuff out, anyway."

My buddy's comments reminded me of one I heard from the diving medical expert, Dr. Tom Neuman. He sums up the reason so many divers end up visiting recompression chambers: "It doesn't matter what dive table you *don't* use!" Perhaps he'd met my buddy.

Divers and Dive Tables

More than 20 years of experience teaching recreational divers has given me a perspective on just why so many otherwise good divers have such difficulty with dive tables. The problem, I believe, is not incompetent instruction. Instructors generally do a good job in teaching new divers how to use dive tables. The problem, instead, stems from divers not retaining what they learn.

Why is it, you ask, that a diver can remember not to hold his breath or how to clear his ears, yet not remember how to use tables that are equally important to his safety? The answer is twofold. First, many people have a basic fear and loathing of numbers. Just ask any math teacher. Furthermore, we're especially afraid of numbers, it seems, when they're placed in columns and rows. As proof, just think back to the last time you had to use an income tax table, or tried to determine how much your mortgage payment would change if you refinanced your home. Not a lot of fun, was it?

The second and more significant reason why so many divers are less than outstanding at using tables is that they rarely have an occasion to use them. Today, most of us dive in organized groups under professional supervision. While this supervision helps ensure safety, it also makes it easy to get lazy with dive tables. In fact, in the vast majority of supervised dives, decisions relating to decompression status (depth, maximum bottom times, surface intervals, etc.) are not made by the diver, but by whomever is supervising him. Add to this the industry estimate that almost half of all divers now use a dive computer, and there's little mystery why a diver's familiarity with tables might get more than a little rusty.

While debate rages over whether dive computers will someday obviate the need for teaching dive tables at all, that's a matter for the future. The reality of today is that responsible divers must be able to think for themselves. Maintaining your ability to use dive tables is a vital part of responsible diving. To re-familiarize you with this essential aspect of safe diving, this chapter will examine the four most popular recreational dive tables and review their procedures for use.

A Word of Caution

This chapter is merely an orientation to four of the most commonly used dive tables. Space limitations prevent addressing all the pertinent rules and special circumstances that can arise in planning an actual dive, such as diving at altitude, safety or decompression stops, and omitted decompression.

Therefore, you should not consider the discussion in this chapter a substitute for professional training in dive-table use by a qualified instructor. Enrolling in a refresher course or continuing education class such as Advanced, Deep, or Multilevel Diving is a great way to learn everything you should know about using dive tables.

INTRODUCTION TO DIVE TABLES

All decompression models in use by recreational divers have a similar conceptual framework. They incorporate one table to tell you your no-decompression limits and how much nitrogen you've absorbed after surfacing; a second table tells you how much of the excess nitrogen you purge while you're on the surface; and still a third table indicates your remaining nitrogen level before you make another dive.

The U.S. Navy Tables

Because they're the granddaddy of most tables in use today, a good place to start any review of use procedures is with the U.S. Navy Tables. With one exception, which we'll discuss later, virtually all other sport diving tables are adaptations of either the USN data or their display format.

Figure 3-1 shows the "No-Decompression Limits and Repetitive Group Destination Table" of the USN Tables. The first left-hand column indicates the depth of the dive. The second column shows the maximum no-decompression limits, expressed in minutes. To determine a repetitive group after a dive, simply find the exact or next greater

FIGURE 3-1

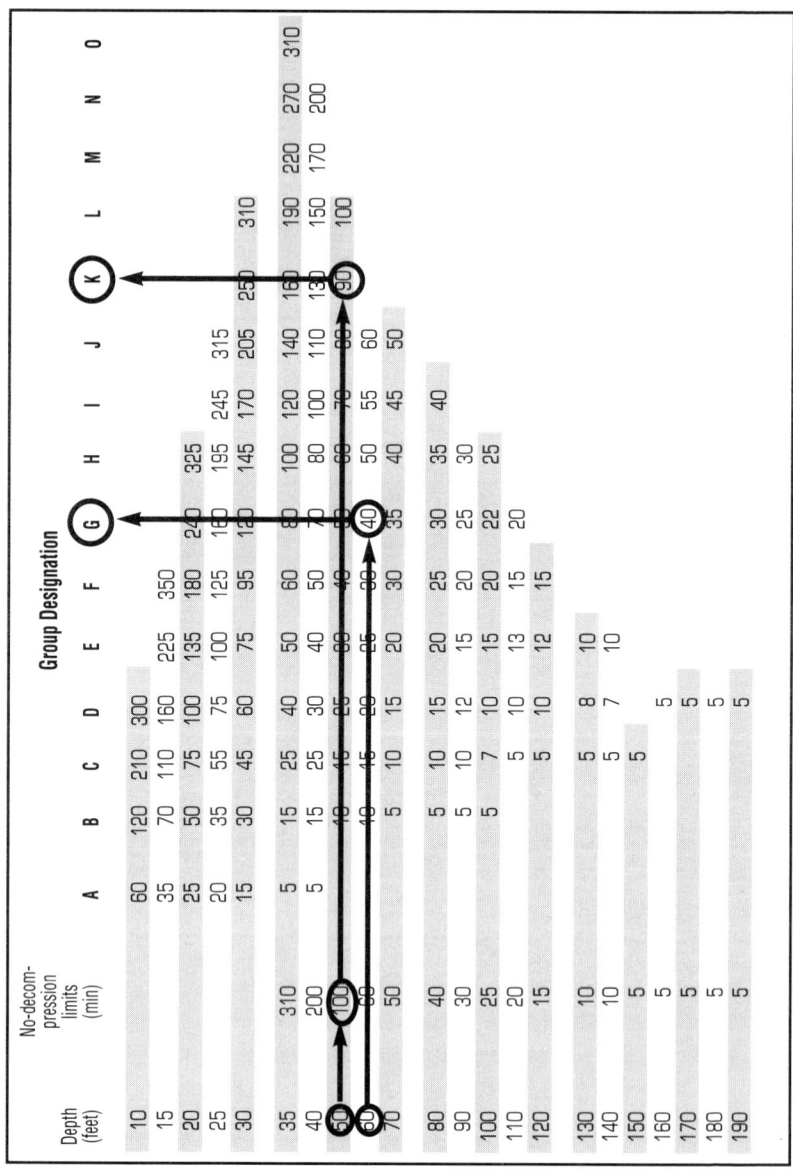

U.S. Navy Table One

FIGURE 3-2

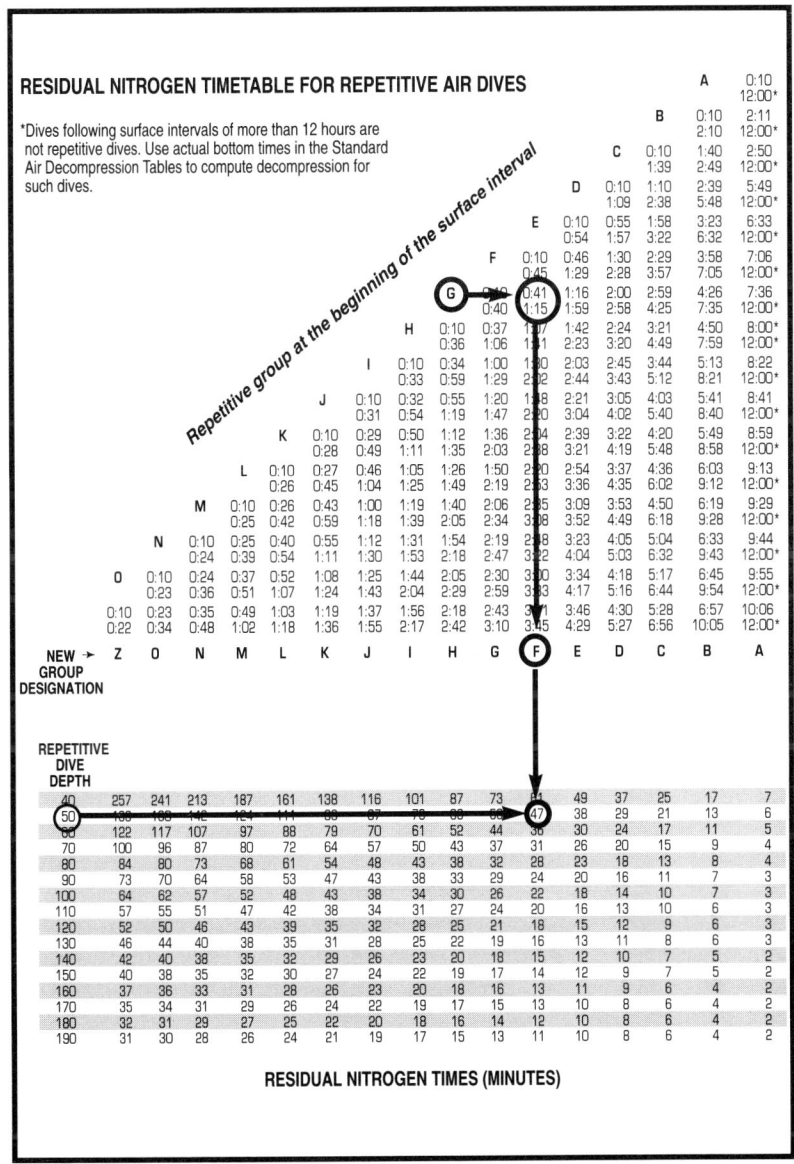

RESIDUAL NITROGEN TIMETABLE FOR REPETITIVE AIR DIVES

*Dives following surface intervals of more than 12 hours are not repetitive dives. Use actual bottom times in the Standard Air Decompression Tables to compute decompression for such dives.

RESIDUAL NITROGEN TIMES (MINUTES)

U.S. Navy Tables Two and Three

depth of your dive. Next, being careful to remain on the correct depth line, move to the right and locate the exact or next greater bottom time of the dive. (The Navy defines bottom time as from the beginning of your descent until the beginning of an uninterrupted ascent directly to the surface.) Once you have located your bottom time, move straight up the column and you will find a "Group Designation," which is a way to quantify the amount of excess or residual nitrogen in your body after a dive

For example, suppose you dived on a shipwreck in 58 feet of water for 32 minutes. This time/depth information is called a "dive profile." As Figure 3-1 illustrates, this profile is considered a 60-foot dive for 40 minutes. Now, move up the column and you'll see you are in repetitive group G. Thus, at the conclusion of your dive, you have excess nitrogen in your body equal to what's defined as a group G. (In the common terminology of dive tables, you're said to be a "G diver".) We'll eventually turn this group letter into a usable number by using the third table.

While at the surface between dives, you'll gradually eliminate the excess nitrogen in your system. Much as a moist sponge dries out over time, you'll eventually lose all your excess nitrogen. But the question is, how much nitrogen will you lose over a given time? This is an important question because you must account for the excess nitrogen in addition to what you'll absorb during your second dive. That's the function of the second table. It tells you how much you'll "dry out" of excess nitrogen.

A brief example will illustrate its use. Let's continue with our previous dive profile. As a G diver after your first dive, let's assume you know it will take at least 45 minutes before you arrive at the next dive site. This time between repetitive dives is call a surface interval. Enter the second table (*Figure 3-2*) along the diagonal row of group letters (not the straight bottom row). The numbers in this table represent time spans, and are expressed as hours and minutes (1:30, for example, means 1 hour and 30 minutes).

Moving to the right from group G, find the box containing your 45-minute surface interval time. Two columns over there's a set of numbers, 0:41 and 1:15. This is a time span from 41 minutes to 1 hour and 15 minutes. As your 45-minute surface interval is within this time span, you'll stop there and move directly down the column. At the bottom of the column you'll find that it ends at a new repetitive group of F. The table has told you that in the span of 45 minutes you have decreased your repetitive group from G at the end of the first dive, to F as you enter on the second dive.

Now it's time to turn our group designation into a number representing how much excess nitrogen is still in our system. This is the function of the third and final table, also illustrated in *Figure 3-2*. Continuing our sample problem, let's assume your second dive will be to a depth of 50 feet. In the lower left corner of *Figure 3-2*, locate the column labeled Repetitive Dive Depth and find the 50-foot depth row. Next, enter the column of numbers directly under group F from the second table, and find where the F column and the 50-foot row intersect. You'll see this occurs at number 47. In this case, the 47 represents time in minutes. More specifically, it represents the excess or residual nitrogen remaining in your system as you reenter the water for your second dive. In other words, even before you make your descent, you already have 47 minutes of "penalty time" credited against you. This penalty time is more formally called *residual nitrogen time*, or RNT.

But how do we put the RNT to practical use? We must return to the first table. If this were the first dive of the day, the first table says you could remain at 50 feet for 100 minutes. However, you have 47 minutes of RNT credited against you, so the maximum no-decompression time for your second dive is only 53 minutes, not the 100 minutes allowed if this was the first dive of the day. It's like having a credit card with a $100 credit limit. If you charged $47 on it, then you could charge only $53 more until you paid off the balance. In a sense, you haven't been on the surface long enough to "pay off" the full balance of your residual nitrogen.

Now let's assume you made the second dive. But rather than spending the full 53 minutes the table allows, you elected to spend only 40 minutes. (Avoiding maximum limits on any dive is always a prudent decision.) As there is not a fourth table, how do you determine your decompression status after the second dive? You must return to the first table, but you must be careful to do so properly. A common mistake is merely to reenter the first table assuming you were at 50 feet for 40 minutes, thus making you an F diver. The problem is that this would ignore the RNT from the first dive and dangerously underestimate your true nitrogen status.

The proper way to return to the first table is by adding your Actual Bottom Time (ABT) to your RNT to arrive at yet another figure called your Total Bottom Time (TBT). In our example, your TBT is 87 minutes (47 RNT plus 40 ABT). This means you'll reenter the first table assuming you were at 50 feet for 90 minutes, not 40 minutes. And this, in turn, puts you in repetitive group K, not group F.

Forgetting to add the ABT to RNT is the single most common error in using dive tables. An easy way to remember this important step is to "always drown the RAT" between dives. This way you're less likely to forget adding your RNT plus ABT to determine TBT (R+A=T).

Seeking to improve decompression safety and make the tables easier to use, a number of organizations have published their own dive tables. Three of the most popular are the NAUI Dive Tables, PADI's Recreational Dive Planner, and DCIEM Sport Diver Tables. Let's take a look at each.

The NAUI Dive Tables

The NAUI Dive Tables are an adaptation of the USN Tables with more conservative no-decompression limits and slightly amended surface interval times. While retaining the three-table format of the USN, the design of the NAUI tables makes them easier to use than the Navy version. Let's use our previous example to illustrate their use.

As with the USN Tables, Table 1 shows that you must interpret a 58-foot dive for 32 minutes as a 60-foot dive for 40 minutes. And, like the USN Tables, this dive will yield a repetitive group of G.

Next, a surface interval of 45 minutes occurs before the second dive. To enter the second table, merely continue to move downward into the G column and, again like the USN Tables, you'll find the time span of 1:15 to 0:41. Moving to the left you now find that you're in a new repetitive group designation of F.

Your second dive has you returning to 50 feet. So, continuing to move to the left, then stopping at the 50-foot column, you again find the 47 minutes of RNT (top number). However, you also have a second number that did not appear on the USN Tables. The bottom, boldface number in the box—33 minutes in this case—is the Adjusted Maximum Dive Time (AMDT). As the term implies, this is the maximum allowable bottom time for your second dive. Note that the sum of these two numbers is always equal to the no-decompression limit for that depth if it had been an initial dive. In this case, the sum is 80, which as Table One shows is the no-decompression limit for 50 feet if this had been the first dive of the day. Providing the AMDT eliminates the need for you to subtract your RNT from the no-decompression limit, as is necessary with the USN Tables.

FIGURE 3-3

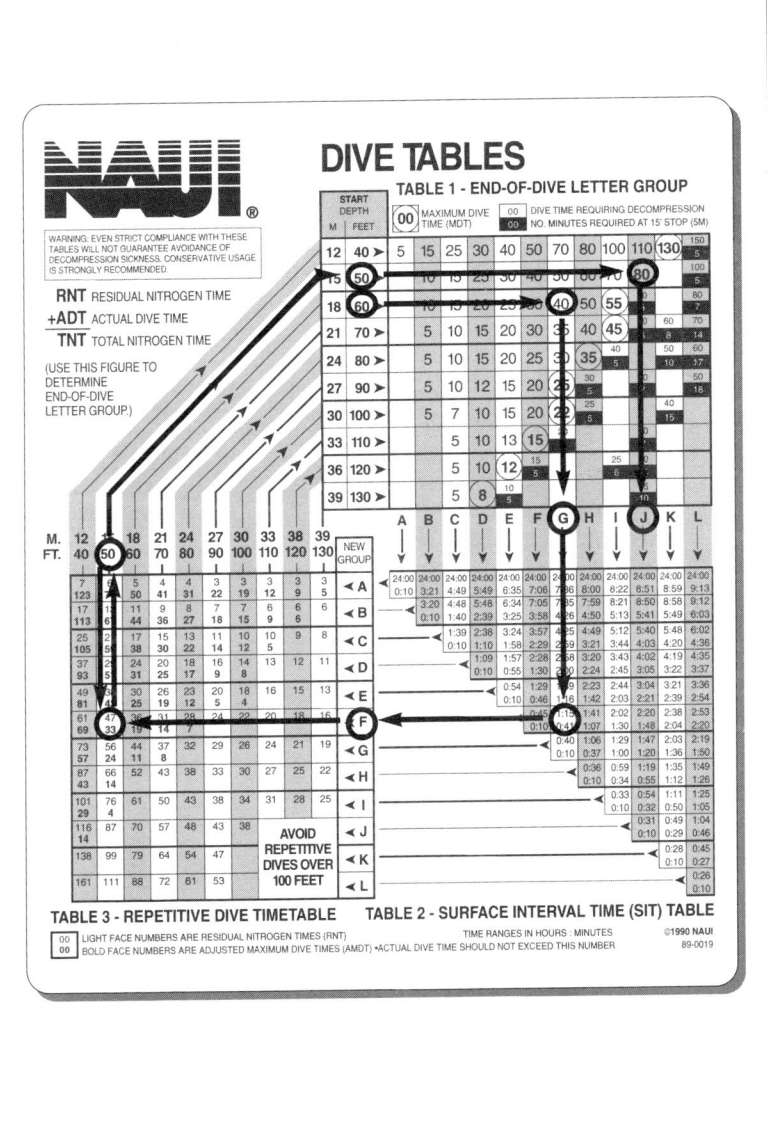

NAUI Tables

In the previous sample using the USN Tables, your second dive was planned for 40 minutes, and you still had 13 minutes to spare before reaching the no-decompression limit. The NAUI Dive Tables, however, allow you only 33 minutes for the second dive. So, when using the NAUI Dive Tables you could not make the second dive for as long as the USN Tables allowed.

Revising our original example, let's plan the second dive for only 30 minutes rather than the 40 minutes we had planned using the USN Tables. Remembering to "always drown the RAT," we calculate your RNT of 47 plus 30 minutes of ABT equals 77 minutes of TBT. To determine your decompression status at the end of the second dive, as illustrated on Figure 3-3, move up the 50-foot column following the line back to Table 1. As your TBT from the dive was 77 minutes, find the exact or greater number from Table 1 along the 50-foot row. This would be 80 minutes. Now move straight down the column and you'll find a new repetitive group of J. If you're making still another dive, simply enter Table Two in the J column and continue as before.

The Recreational Dive Planner

Unlike the NAUI Dive Tables, PADI's Recreational Dive Planner (RDP) is not based completely upon the USN model. Although the conceptual design of the RDP is similar in approach to the Navy's, the RDP was independently developed and tested by the Diving Science and Technology Corporation (DSAT). Like the NAUI Tables and other more recent tables and computers, the RDP has shorter no-decompression limits than the USN Tables. A significant difference between the RDP and other tables, as explained in the last chapter, is the faster controlling tissue compartment the model uses during surface intervals. (We'll see an example of this later.) Regarding its format and use, however, the RDP continues the familiar three-table approach.

Let's return to the original sample dive profile to illustrate how to use the RDP. You have descended to 58 feet for 32 minutes. Locate the Start position on the RDP [Figure 3-4]. There you'll find the depth row. Find the 60-foot column and move straight down to 32 or the next greater number, in this case 33. Stop there and move horizontally to the right, and you find you are now in repetitive group M.

Your surface interval is 45 minutes. Continuing to move to the right, you'll locate the box with the time span of 0:40 to 0:46. Now, move straight down the column and you'll come to a new repetitive group of F.

FIGURE 3-4

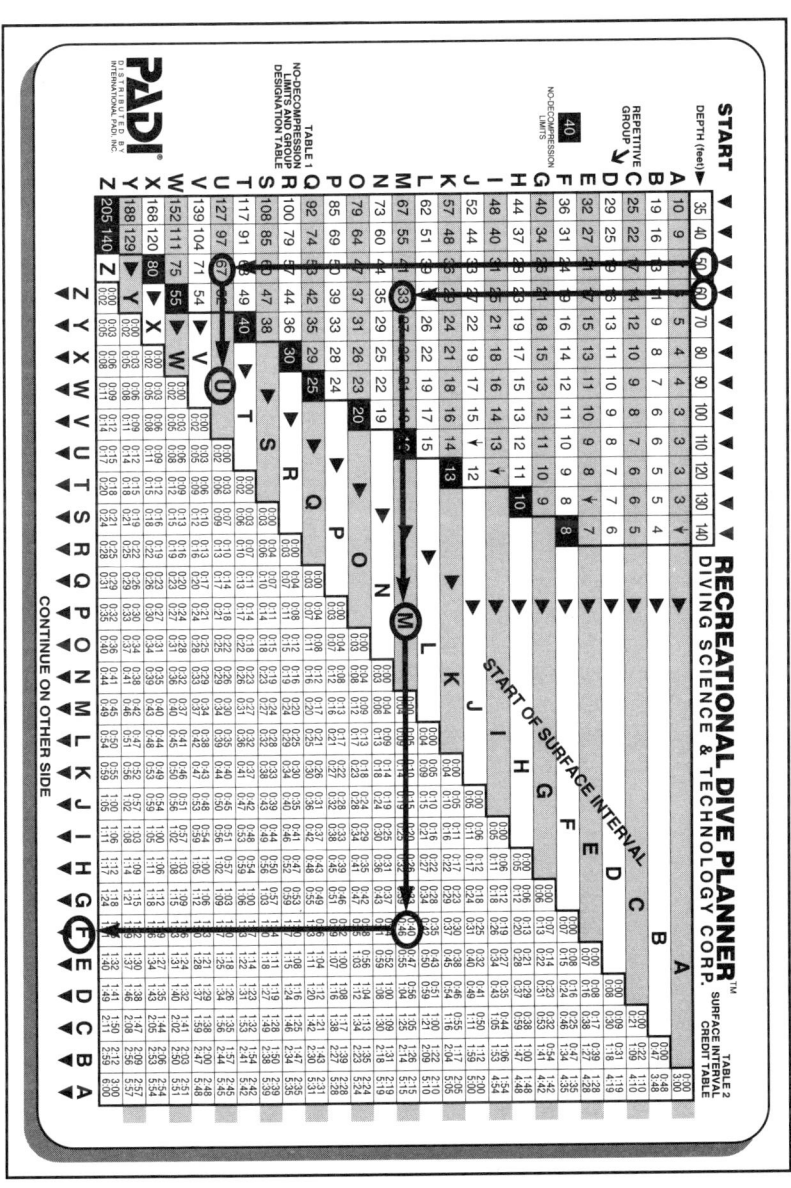

Recreational Dive Planner, side one

FIGURE 3-5

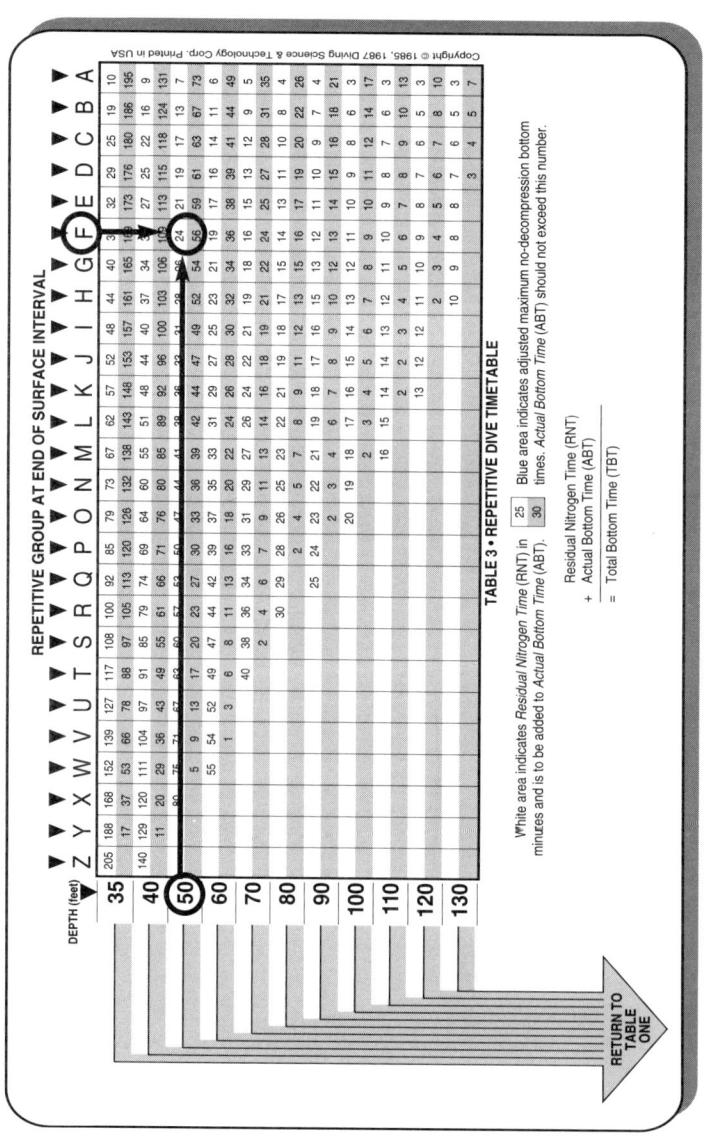

Recreational Dive Planner, side two

Next, turn the RDP over to side two and find the F column at the top, as shown in *Figure 3-5*. Locate the depth column on the extreme left end. Move horizontally to the right along the 50-foot row until you find the box that intersects with the group F column. This box contains the numbers 24 at the top white portion and 56 in the bottom dark portion. Here the 24 represents the RNT, while the 56 is the Adjusted No-Decompression Limit or ANDL (analogous to the AMDT on the NAUI Dive Tables). This is the maximum allowable time for the second dive.

Although you could stay for 56 minutes, your second dive is actually only 40 minutes. Remember to "always drown the rat:" 24 minutes of RNT from Table Three plus the 40-minute ABT equals a TBT of 64 minutes.

To determine your decompression status at the end of the second dive, you must return to side one *[Figure 3-4]* and locate the 50-foot depth column. Moving down the column you find that, as there is no 64, you must select the next greater number, which is 67. Moving horizontally to the right you quickly determine that your repetitive group after the second dive is U. Incidentally, although both the RDP model and the USN/NAUI models use alphabets to indicate a certain level of residual nitrogen, the actual levels corresponding to identical letters are vastly different. Therefore, *you cannot interchange repetitive groups among the RDP and USN/NAUI tables.* Once you begin using a particular table, never switch to a different table to plan a repetitive dive.

The DCIEM Tables

The DCIEM Sport Diving Tables, distributed by Universal Dive Techtronics of Toronto, were derived from the air decompression model developed in 1983 by Canada's Defence and Civil Institute of Environmental Medicine (DCIEM). The DCIEM model was based, in part, on earlier work by researchers Kidd and Stubbs, whose model differed from the more traditional Haldanean model in the number and presumed arrangement of the mathematical compartments.

Although the DCIEM Tables are relatively new to the recreational diving community, scientific, commercial, and technical divers have used them for a number of years. Today most of the North American-based diver training organizations, along with a number of governments and naval authorities around the world, have approved the DCIEM Tables for use.

Not only do the DCIEM Tables differ from the USN Tables in the theoretical design, they also differ in their format and use. Again, using

FIGURE 3-6

DCIEM SPORT DIVING TABLES

A: AIR DECOMPRESSION

Depth		No-Decompression Bottom Times (minutes)				Decompression Required Bottom Times			
20'	6m	30 A 60 B 90 C 120 D	150 E 180 F 240 G 300 H	360 I 420 J 480 K 600 L	720 M ∞				
30'	9m	30 A 45 B 60 C 90 D	100 E 120 F 150 G 180 H	190 I 210 J 240 K 270 L	300 M	360	400		
40'	12m	22 A 30 B 40 C	60 D 70 E 80 F	90 G 120 H 130 I	150 J	160 K 170 L	180 M 190	200	215
50'	15m	18 A 25 B	30 C 40 D	50 E	75 G	85 H 95 I	105 J 115 K	124 L	132 M
60'	18m	14 A 20 B	25 C 30 D	40 E	50 F	60 G	70 H 80 I	85 J	92 K
Decompression Stops in minutes					at 10' 3m	5	10	15	20
70'	21m	12 A 15 B	20 C	25 D	35 E	40 F	50 G	60 H 63 I	66 J
80'	24m	10 A 13 B	15 C	20 D	25 E	29 F	35 G	48 H	52 I
90'	27m	9 A	12 B	15 C	20 D	23 E	27 F	35 G	40 H 43 I
100'	30m	7 A	10 B	12 C	15 D	18 D	21 E	25 F 29 G	36 H
110'	33m		6 A	10 B	12 C	15 D	18 E	22 F	26 G 30 H
120'	36m		6 A	8 B	10 C	12 D	15 E	19 F	25 G
130'	39m			5 A	8 B	10 C	13 D	16 F	21 G
140'	42m			5 A	7 B	9 C	11 D	14 F	18 G
150'	45m			4 A	6 B	8 C	10 D	12 E	15 F
Decompression Stops in minutes					at 20' 6m	-	-	5	10
					at 10' 3m	5	10	10	10

- **ASCENT RATE** is 60' (18m) plus or minus 10' (3m) per minute
- **NO-DECOMPRESSION LIMITS** are given for first dives
- **DECOMPRESSION STOPS** are taken at mid-chest level for the times indicated at the specified stop depths
- → Table B for **Minimum Surface Intervals** and Repetitive Factors
- → Table C for **Repetitive Dive No-Decompression Limits**
- → Table D for **Depth Corrections** required at Altitudes above 1000' (300m)

The Department of National Defence (Canada), Defence and Civil Institute of Environmental Medicine (DCIEM), and Universal Dive Techtronics, Inc. (UDT), disclaim any and all responsibilities for the use of the DCIEM Sport Diving Tables and procedures.
© Her Majesty the Queen in Right of Canada 1990.

DCIEM Table A

FIGURE 3-7

B: SURFACE INTERVALS

Rep. Group	0:15 / 0:29	0:30 / 0:59	1:00 / 1:29	1:30 / 1:59	2:00 / 2:59	3:00 / 3:59	4:00 / 5:59	6:00 / 8:59	9:00 / 11:59	12:00 / 14:59	15:00 / 18:00
A	1.4	1.2	1.1	1.1	1.1	1.1	1.1	1.1	1.1	1.0	1.0
B	1.5	1.3	1.2	1.2	1.2	1.1	1.1	1.1	1.1	1.0	1.0
C	1.6	1.4	1.3	1.2	1.2	1.2	1.1	1.1	1.1	1.0	1.0
D	1.8	1.5	1.4	1.3	1.3	1.2	1.2	1.1	1.1	1.0	1.0
E	1.9	1.6	1.5	1.4	1.3	1.3	1.2	1.2	1.1	1.1	1.0
F	2.0	1.7	1.6	1.5	1.4	1.3	1.3	1.2	1.1	1.1	1.0
G	-	1.9	1.7	1.6	1.5	1.4	1.3	1.2	1.1	1.1	1.0
H	-	-	1.9	1.7	1.6	1.5	1.4	1.3	1.1	1.1	1.1
I	-	-	2.0	1.8	1.7	1.5	1.4	1.3	1.1	1.1	1.1
J	-	-	-	1.9	1.8	1.6	1.5	1.3	1.2	1.1	1.1
K	-	-	-	2.0	1.9	1.7	1.5	1.3	1.2	1.1	1.1
L	-	-	-	-	2.0	1.7	1.6	1.4	1.2	1.1	1.1
M	-	-	-	-	-	1.8	1.6	1.4	1.2	1.1	1.1

Repetitive Factors (RF) given for Surface Intervals (hr:min)

C: REPETITIVE DIVING

Depth		1.1	1.2	1.3	1.4	1.5	1.6	1.7	1.8	1.9	2.0
30'	9m	272	250	230	214	200	187	176	166	157	150
40'	12m	136	125	115	107	100	93	88	83	78	75
50'	15m	66	55	50	45	41	38	36	34	32	31
60'	18m	40	35	31	29	27	26	24	23	22	21
70'	21m	30	25	21	19	18	17	16	15	14	13
80'	24m	20	18	16	15	14	13	12	12	11	11
90'	27m	16	14	12	11	11	11	10	9	9	8
100'	30m	13	11	10	9	9	8	8	7	7	7
110'	33m	10	9	8	8	7	7	6	6	6	6
120'	36m	8	7	7	6	6	6	5	5	5	5
130'	39m	7	6	6	5	5	5	4	4	4	4
140'	42m	6	5	5	5	4	4	4	3	3	3
150'	45m	5	5	4	4	4	3	3	3	3	3

Repetitive Dive No-D Limits given in minutes according to Depth and RF

D: DEPTH CORRECTIONS

Actual Depth		1000' →1999 / 300m →599		2000' →2999 / 600m →899		3000' →3999 / 900m →1199		4000' →4999 / 1200m →1499		5000' →5999 / 1500m →1799		6000' →6999 / 1800m →2099		7000' →7999 / 2100m →2399		8000' →10000 / 2400m →3000	
30'	9m	10	3	10	3	10	3	10	3	10	3	10	3	20	6	20	6
40'	12m	10	3	10	3	10	3	10	3	10	3	20	6	20	6	20	6
50'	15m	10	3	10	3	10	3	10	3	20	6	20	6	20	6	20	6
60'	18m	10	3	10	3	10	3	20	6	20	6	20	6	20	6	30	9
70'	21m	10	3	10	3	10	3	20	6	20	6	20	6	30	9	30	9
80'	24m	10	3	10	3	20	6	20	6	20	6	30	9	30	9	40	12
90'	27m	10	3	10	3	20	6	20	6	20	6	30	9	30	9	40	12
100'	30m	10	3	10	3	20	6	20	6	30	9	30	9	30	9	40	12
110'	33m	10	3	20	6	20	6	20	6	30	9	30	9	40	12		
120'	36m	10	3	20	6	20	6	30	9	30	9	30	9				
130'	39m	10	3	20	6	20	6										
140'	42m	10	3														

Add Depth Correction to Actual Depth of Altitude Dive

10'	3m	10	3.0	10	3.0	9	3.0	9	3.0	9	3.0	8	2.5	8	2.5	8	2.5
20'	6m	20	6.0	19	6.0	18	5.5	18	5.5	17	5.0	16	5.0	16	5.0	15	4.5

Actual Decompression Stop Depths (feet/*metres*) at Altitude

Published under government license by Universal Dive Technronics, Inc. Ste. 201 — 2691 Viscount Way, Richmond, B.C., CANADA, V6V 1M9

DCIEM Tables B, C, and D

Why Do Tables Give Different Limits?

You've undoubtedly noticed that the four tables discussed in this chapter each give differing results regarding the same dive profile. Divers often ask, "How is this possible?"

The answer has to do with the fact that dive tables and computers differ in their scope and intent. For example, the Navy constructed its dive tables for decompression diving, meaning it expected the diver would intentionally exceed the no-stop limit. A decompression model must assume that "slow" tissue compartments load with much higher nitrogen levels than for a no-decompression model. Any table designed for decompression diving (as well as any table derived from a decompression model) must also take into account that a repetitive dive may be preceded—and in some models even followed—by a decompression dive. Therefore, a decompression table must mandate long surface intervals to allow the slow compartments to unload the high level of nitrogen absorbed on a decompression dive. These long surface intervals, however, occur regardless of whether the previous dive was a decompression or no-decompression dive.

Conversely, the RDP is a special application table intended solely for no-decompression (no-stop) diving. This is an important distinction because, according to DSAT researchers, in most cases a no-decompression model does not have to be limited by the lengthy outgassing process required by the slower compartments of a decompression model. What's the practical consequence of all this? In a no-decompression model, because a repetitive dive is never preceded by a

---

the same sample dive profile as before, you're making a dive to 58 feet for 32 minutes. As shown in *Figure 3-6*, you begin with Table A. As you did with the other tables, locate the exact or next greater depth. The depth column is at the extreme left. In this case you should select 60 feet.

Next, move to the right and you'll find four boxes under the heading "No-Decompression Bottom Times." Again locate the exact or next greater number—in this case, 40. Next to the number 40 is the letter E. This is your repetitive group, and you'll use this letter to enter Table B, shown in *Figure 3-7*.

Your surface interval is 45 minutes. The row at the top of Table B represents time spans. Here, as in our previous examples, the table expresses time in the familiar hour and minute format. Column two indicates the time span of between 30 minutes (0:30) and 59 minutes

decompression dive, the surface interval does not need to be as restrictive as in a decompression model. This means the resulting no-decompression limits for a repetitive dive are less restrictive as well.

This idea was pioneered in the mid-1980s by the RDP's developer, Dr. Raymond Rogers, and validated by test trials in both the chamber and open sea. The hundreds of thousands of dives performed using the RDP since then demonstrate a pragmatic success of Rogers' approach for recreational diving.

The trend in both recreational and technical diving is toward special tables dedicated to particular needs. The is exactly what the RDP is—a no-decompression repetitive dive table.

Although the other tables examined in this chapter are used by recreational divers for no-decompression diving, they were derived from models that make decompression diving possible.

Furthermore, it's incorrect to determine the relative safety of dive tables by comparing numbers and assuming that the more conservative is the safest. The only way to determine the safety of a dive table is by evaluating its ability to prevent DCS. Given our limited understanding of the decompression phenomenon, all of the tables examined in this chapter have been shown to do a good job of prevention when they are used correctly.

Ultimately, what's important are not the differences in the dive tables, but that you plan your dive properly by using whatever table you decide is most appropriate for you.

(0:59). Your 45-minute surface interval falls within this span, so this is the column you should use. This column intersects the E-group row at a box containing the number 1.6. You will use this number to calculate the amount of excess or residual nitrogen in your body. It's called a Repetitive Factor or simply RF. The highest RF is 2.0, and the number decreases as your surface interval increases.

A repetitive dive is any dive where your RF is greater than 1.0. Thus, if your RF is 1.0 or less, merely go back to Table A to plan your next dive. If your RF is greater than 1.0, enter Table C. In our example, your RF is 1.6, so, you'll enter Table C *[Figure 3-7]*.

Enter Table C from the depth column at the extreme left. As your second dive is to a depth of 50 feet, find the 50-foot row. Next, locate your RF of 1.6 along the top row, then find the box where the 50-foot row and 1.6 column intersect. This is at the box containing the number

38. You have just determined that you could remain for as long as 38 minutes on your second dive.

Finally, how do you determine your decompression status after the second dive? This is vitally important if you plan to make still another dive. Let's assume, for example, that although you could have remained at 50 feet for 38 minutes, you chose to stay only 30 minutes on your second dive. To determine your decompression status you must return to Table A. But to do so, you must first determine your Effective Bottom Time (EBT) for the second dive. To do this multiply the bottom time of your second dive by the RF of 1.6. In your case, 30 minutes times 1.6 equals an EBT of 48 minutes. (You can also determine EBT with a special table that accompanies the DCIEM Tables; a copy is also included in the instruction booklet.)

Back on Table A, locate the 50-foot row. Moving to the right you find that 50 is the next greater number to your 48-minute EBT. Your repetitive group after the second dive, which appears next to the number 50, is E.

Unlike the other tables we've looked at, the DCIEM Tables contain a depth correction table for use at altitude (Table D in *Figure 3-7*). Although you can use other tables at altitude, they will require various conversion factors or special procedures not found on the tables themselves. This self-contained altitude capability is handy for those who regularly dive 1,000 feet or more above sea level.

SOME PARTING WORDS

According to statistics from the Divers Alert Network, somewhere between 700 and 800 recreational divers seek hyperbaric treatment for decompression illness each year. You could conclude that, given the millions of dives made each year, the risk of injury while diving is quite low (a risk comparable to bowling, according to one recent study). Yet, if you are the person who is bent, even one accident is too many.

Although proper use of dive tables cannot guarantee you will avoid DCS, you are a lot less likely to become a statistic by learning to use dive tables correctly and conservatively. There is no clearer application of what your mama used to say: "An ounce of prevention is worth a pound of cure."

CHAPTER FOUR

Turning on a Computer Shouldn't Mean Turning Off Your Brain

Using Dive Computers Wisely

Most of us have grown up depending on technology. It brews our morning coffee, operates the computer we use at work, and controls the jumbo jet that whisks us away to exotic diving locations. We are, in fact, so dependent upon technology that we usually accept it even if we don't understand it. Yet, an uninformed acceptance sometimes keeps us from enjoying its full benefits, and in some cases can be outright dangerous.

As divers, when we think of high technology what usually comes to mind are dive computers. In only a few years, the number of divers using computers has exploded to an unimagined level. Today about half of all recreational divers use one. The reason is simple. These wondrous little devices have helped free us of the tedious burden—and potential human error—of using dive tables. They also provide certain advantages that many dive tables cannot, such as keeping track of your decompression status during a multilevel dive.

To use a dive computer wisely means we must understand it. In learning about dive computers, once we get beyond understanding their operating procedures, a lot of basic questions arise. In the first part of this chapter we'll look at where the idea for dive computers came from, and how the idea evolved into the instruments we use today. Next, we'll explore what's inside those little black boxes, how they work, and why they often vary from model to model in the information they give you. We'll also discuss how to make an informed decision when you purchase one.

In the second part of the chapter we'll move from the realm of theory to practice. We'll first look at the important difference between computer-*assisted* versus computer-*dependent* diving, and examine both the capabilities and limitations of dive computers. The final segment will delve into practical "how-to" techniques for using your computer in a safe and responsible manner.

A QUICK AND DIRTY HISTORY

Divers are often surprised to find out that the idea of a mechanical device to determine decompression status is quite old—much older than the microprocessor.

Before Microprocessors—The Stone Age

A U.S. Navy report submitted in 1953 suggested the development of a mechanical device to monitor the decompression and air consumption of the new "underwater swimmers"—their name for scuba divers. The report even provided a basic design for such a device.

In 1955, following the advice of the Navy's report, the Foxboro Electronics Corporation developed a prototype device. Dubbed the Foxboro Decomputer Mark I, it was a pneumatic design that used a system of springs, bellows, and porous resistors to simulate nitrogen absorption and elimination. It contained two tissue compartments— 40 and 75 minutes. Unfortunately, the Navy Experimental Diving Unit (EDU) found that the Mark I was inconsistent with Navy decompression tables. The Navy returned the device for redesign; Foxboro never resubmitted it for further evaluation. But, the project proved the practicality of a dive computer.

The next mechanical dive computer was one that many recreational divers of the 1960s and '70s probably remember—the SOS Meter. It was designed and manufactured by the SOS Diving Equipment Company of Italy in 1959 and distributed initially in the U.S. by the Healthways Corporation, and later by the Scubapro Corporation.

PHOTO 4-1

The first dive computer to enjoy commercial success, the SOS Decompression Meter was a nondigital, pneumatic device. But, after empirical testing, serious questions arose about its safety.

The SOS Meter was a wrist-mounted device made of plastic (later of stainless steel) and looked like a wind-up alarm clock. It operated on a "single-tissue" concept. Upon descent, increasing pressure compressed a flexible gas-filled bag. The compression squeezed gas through a porous, ceramic element into a constant volume chamber. The rate of gas exchange through this element, the designers assumed, was the same as nitrogen absorption in the body. On ascent, the pressure in the constant volume chamber increased, and gas passed back into the bag via the ceramic element. This rate was assumed to be the same as nitrogen elimination in the body.

Although used by thousands of divers for many years, serious concerns arose after scientific evaluation of the device. Test results showed the SOS Meter to be more conservative than the U.S. Navy Dive Table limits on dives shallower than 60 feet. But it was less conservative on dives deeper than 60 feet. The device is no longer distributed in the U.S., although it's still available in Europe.

In 1962 important research into dive computer technology began at the Canadian Forces Institute of Aviation Medicine and Canadian Defence Medical Laboratory in Toronto (the forerunner of DCIEM) by Kidd and Stubbs. By 1965 they developed the pneumatic analog decompression computer (PADC). It used the four-compartment Kidd-Stubbs decompression model (see Chapter Two). Extensive tests revealed this device to be highly effective. Manufactured for commercial and military use, the PADC was never intended for the recreational diving market. It was expensive and needed extensive maintenance.

The first electronic analog (nondigital) decompression computer was developed by Texas Research Associates in 1963. Dubbed the

TRACOR Electronic Analog Computer, it used a series of electronic resistors and capacitors to simulate absorption and elimination of nitrogen in the human body. Once again, an evaluation by the Navy EDU found the device gave inadequate decompression, particularly for long, deep dives. The evaluation also pointed up the most significant factor complicating the development of electronic dive computers—the sensitivity of electronic componentry to extreme temperatures. The temperature ranges encountered by divers presented enormous technical problems, which wouldn't be solved for almost 20 years.

In 1973 General Electric offered a new approach to the problem. To simulate nitrogen absorption and elimination, GE used semipermeable silicon membranes. It developed a four-tissue compartment device that tests showed to be highly effective in simulating the U.S. Navy decompression schedules. For unexplained reasons, however, GE did not continue development of the device.

Picking up on the semipermeable silicon technology, Farallon Industries, a diving equipment manufacturer, in 1975 developed a device similar to GE's. Dubbed the Decomputer, this was the first dive computer introduced to recreational divers since the SOS Meter in the late 1950s. The Decomputer used a two-tissue decompression model. A gas-filled bag, when subjected to pressure, forced air across two membranes—one "fast" and one "slow." On ascent the expanding gas passed through the "offgassing membrane," simulating nitrogen elimination. Unfortunately, during independent testing this device gave no-decompression limits in excess of the U.S. Navy Tables.

All Hail the Microprocessor!

By the late 1970s and early 1980s important technological advances revolutionized dive computers. Low-cost microprocessors with minimal power requirements had become commonplace. And designers solved the temperature sensitivity problem of pressure transducers. (A pressure transducer is a device that senses external pressure and converts it into an electronic current.) The pieces of the puzzle needed to solve the dive computer dilemma were ready.

One method of using microprocessors is to program a decompression model into the memory of the computer. This type of device is called *model-based*. Using time and pressure (depth) information, the microprocessor computes the diver's decompression status by using a set of mathematical instructions (called an *algorithm*) imprinted on a computer chip. An algorithm is merely an equation or series of mathematical steps designed for a specific task—such as computing nitrogen absorption and elimination.

Another way of using microprocessor technology, although not quite as useful, is to program actual dive tables into the computer's memory. The device then "reads" the tables according to the depth and duration of the dive. This type of computer is called *table-based*.

The earliest work with digital microprocessors occurred in the mid-'70s at DCIEM under the direction of scientist Ron Nishi and resulted in the XDC Digital Decompression Computer series. The XDC-1 was a desktop dive calculator programmed with the highly successful Kidd-Stubbs decompression model. The device was not carried underwater, but instead was used for planning and analyzing dive profiles.

The next generation—the XDC-2—required less maintenance and calibration. Although still not a diver-carried device, it was designed for surface-supplied diving and hyperbaric chamber operations. Later programmed with the DCIEM 1983 decompression model, the XDC-2 was used in validating the DCIEM tables discussed in Chapter Two.

The XDC-3, a diver-carried device, solved the problem of free-swimming scuba divers. It provided most of the information of the XDC-2 but operated on batteries. The drawback was that, because low-power components and digital displays were not available at the time, the XDC-3 had an enormous power requirement. In cold water it could drain four 9-volt transistor batteries in only four hours. This expense and inconvenience made the XDC-3 impractical for most recreational divers to use.

In 1978, Kybertec International, a company that spun off from a firm involved in developing the XDC series, designed and marketed the Cyberdiver. A variation of the XDC-3, designers programmed the Cyberdiver to read the U.S. Navy Tables. The device connected to the diver's high-pressure hose and also provided a read-out of tank pressure. Using only one standard 9-volt battery, it was a more practical device for recreational divers than the XDC series. The next generation—the Cyberdiver II—went back to the model-based approach using the reliable Kidd-Stubbs decompression model.

Unfortunately, the Cyberdiver series was expensive, bulky, required periodic recalibration, and was plagued by a water leakage problem. Only about 700 units were sold, and the device was discontinued in the early 1980s. However, the introduction of the Cyberdiver was an important milestone in the evolution of dive computers. Exposure to the device, although limited, was one of the factors that sparked interest in computer technology among recreational divers.

In the late '70s, the Dacor Corporation returned to the table-based approach for a short-lived project to create its first dive computer—the DDC. Like the Cyberdiver II, the DDC read the U.S. Navy Dive Tables according to the diver's actual dive profile. Like other devices of the time, the DDC was power hungry, requiring special expensive batteries. For this reason, and due to the inability

PHOTO 4-2

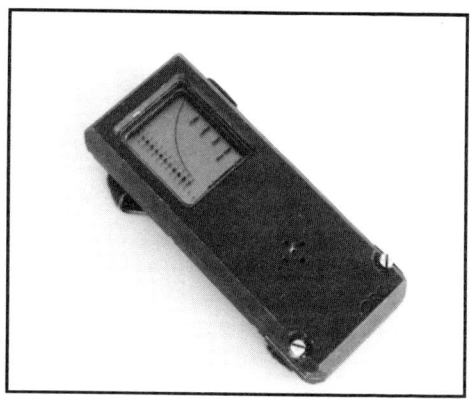

The Edge, manufactured by Orca Industries, was one of the first microprocessor-based dive computers used extensively by recreational divers.

to purchase enough memory chips, the DDC was never mass-produced.

In 1983 the first commercially successful microprocessor dive computers were introduced. These were the Edge, produced by U.S.-based Orca Industries, and the Decobrain I, produced by the European-based Divetronic Corporation.

Each took a different approach to solving the decompression problem. The Edge was a Haldanean model-based device. Decobrain I was table-based using the high altitude tables of Dr. Albert Buhlmann, a researcher at the University of Zurich. Divetronic later introduced a model-based version—the Decobrain II—along with several software upgrades. (Buhlmann's decompression model, or some variation, is the basis of most dive computers with high altitude capabilities.)

Soon after the introduction of the Edge and Decobrain, several other manufacturers introduced dive computers. A collaborative effort between Oceanic and the U.S. Divers Company resulted in a device that displayed both the diver's decompression and air-supply status. The Oceanic version was called the DataMaster II, and the U.S. Divers model the Data Scan 2.

From these preliminary devices many refinements and innovations have occurred. Today about two dozen models are available. Some provide only minimal no-decompression information. Others give extensive decompression provisions allowing dives far beyond the recreational diving limit of 130 feet. Many computers now have downloading capabilities. This means that with the proper connecting hardware, the data collected can be transferred to a desktop computer to log and analyze the dive profile.

The most recent dive computers allow the user to change some of the parameters in the program, such as the percentage of oxygen in the diver's gas mixture. Although this is an irrelevant feature for recreational divers, it does accommodate the needs of the growing number of technical divers who use altered gas mixtures, such as enriched air nitrox.

THE ANATOMY OF A DIVE COMPUTER

While divers have lots of models from which to choose, virtually all dive computers on the market today work in the same basic way. Schematically, dive computers contain eight elemental components. (See *Figure 4-1*).

Power source: This provides the electrical power for all other components. As dive computers vary significantly in their power requirements, the power supplies differ greatly. Some use extreme long-life batteries that must be replaced by the manufacturer or dealer. Others use shorter life, user-replaceable batteries. For this reason, the type and amount of diving you do and the availability of technical support should be important criteria in selecting a computer.

Display: Like the power supply, this component differs widely among the various models. The display tells divers their decompression status and, if so designed, other vital information. Usually, the display reads out only the status of the controlling tissue compartment. While underwater, all devices provide a depth read-out and remaining no-decompression time. Should the diver exceed the no-decompression limits, the device provides information for the depth and time of required decompression stops. A few computers graphically display how much nitrogen your body has absorbed. Once at the surface, it also tracks outgassing. The diver gets his decompression status as constantly changing no-decompression times. Usually, the display scrolls the information throughout the surface interval so the diver has a way of planning a repetitive dive.

Internal clock: This keeps track of bottom time and surface intervals. The internal clock also dictates the rate at which the computer

FIGURE 4-1

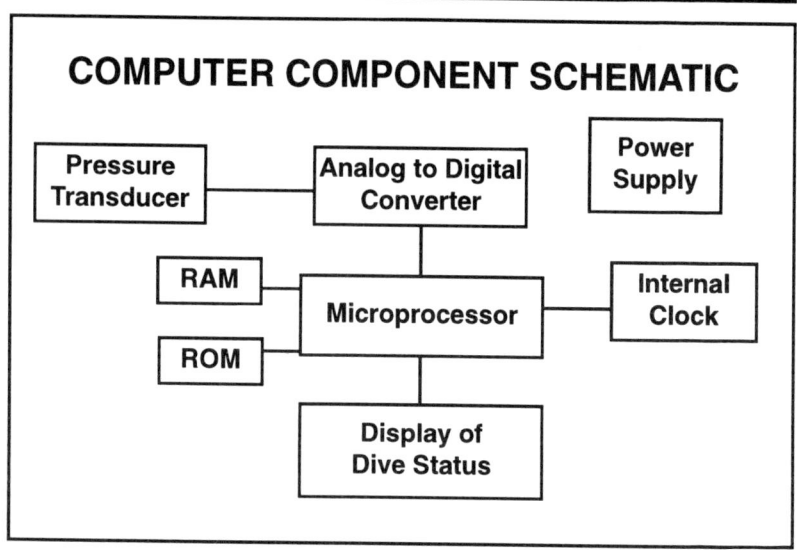

COMPUTER COMPONENT SCHEMATIC

A schematic of a modern dive computer.

calculations take place. An advantage of digital technology is that it's more accurate than most analog timepieces.

Pressure transducer: This component senses the ambient pressure, then converts it into an electrical current. The voltage of the current varies according to the amount of pressure sensed.

Analog-to-digital (A/D) converter: The basic language of all computers is the binary or digital code. The electrical current from the pressure transducer, therefore, must first be transformed into a digital signal. Only then can the computer make sense out of the information provided by the transducer. The A/D converter does this, making the information provided by the transducer readable to the computer.

Read Only Memory (ROM): A silicone microchip, this component contains the instructions for the computer. Information encrypted on the chip is unalterable except by the manufacturer. It contains information such as the compartment half-times and M-values of the decompression model. It also tells the microprocessor what steps to perform.

Random Access Memory (RAM): This component stores the dive data and the results of the various calculations made by the microprocessor. Information stored here is what the device processes as it scrolls during the surface interval or downloads to a desktop computer.

Microprocessor: This is the brain of the dive computer. It takes information from the A/D converter, along with input from ROM and RAM, and performs all the mathematical computations.

How Computers Handle Calculations

While all dive computers are similar in the way they operate, there are important differences in how they derive information. We have already seen how model-based devices differ from table-based ones. Now let's look at a few other important differences.

One term often used to describe computer models is *modified Haldanean*. Actually this term is a poor description. With one exception, all dive computers on the market today use essentially a modification of Haldane's original decompression model. The modifications usually involve the specific values and number of half-times and the maximum allowable surfacing pressures (M-values). All dive computers use M-values more conservative than those used in the U.S. Navy Tables.

The other term sometimes used to describe computer models is *table-based*. As explained earlier, this refers to a computer that reads a set of dive tables programmed into its memory. Except for a timepiece produced by a popular watch manufacturer, however, table-based computers have been discontinued because of their extreme conservatism.

A better means of describing the models used in dive computers is by examining how it handles offgasing. There are two distinct approaches. One assumes that offgasing occurs exponentially—the same way ongasing occurrs. As we saw in the last chapter, this is sometimes called the *E-E model,* meaning "exponential in/exponential out."

E-E model-based devices control repetitive dives by whatever tissue compartment is in control at the moment. For example, let's assume a diver is planning a series of dives to 120 feet. (This example was chosen to illustrate a theory; such deep repetitive diving isn't a wise idea as an actual practice.) The 5-minute compartment normally controls no-decompression dives to this depth. If the diver planned to return to 120 feet for a repetitive dive, an E-E model computer will base surface outgassing on the 5-minute compartment as well. This means the model assumes the diver's nitrogen level will drop very quickly. Thus, the device allows another dive to 120 feet after only a short surface interval. The problem is that practical experience and controlled stud-

Which is the Best Computer to Buy?

With the proliferation of dive computers, how do you know which one to buy? This is much like asking, "Which car should I buy?" While you'll get a lot of different opinions, the only reasonable answer is, "It depends." Just as no single car could possibly suit the needs of every driver, no single computer could possibly suit the needs of every diver.

Each diver must answer the question of "which is best" for himself or herself, based on a myriad practical factors. For example, which type of diving do you do most often—shallow? deep? multilevel? Is it important that your computer handle decompression as well as no-decompression situations? Do you want the computer to monitor your air supply? Is the life of the battery, and who can replace it, an important consideration? How much information would you like to recall for logging purposes; do you want to be able to download to a personal computer? How much will the computer cost, and what kind of follow-up service can you expect?

Beating the Bends is not about computers but rather how to avoid DCS. So, it's beyond the scope of our discussion to cover individual devices. Besides, as with most technology, it changes so fast that by the time such information is in

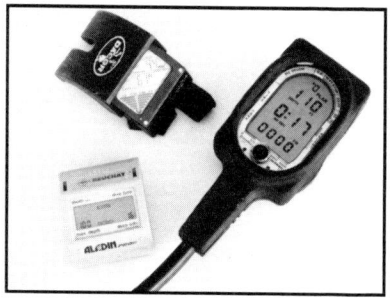

The "best" computer is the one that meets your personal needs. All dive computers will do their job—if used properly. Remember, no mechanical device can take the place of good ol' common sense.

print, it's already outdated. For the most up-to-date facts about the models currently on the market, see your local dive store—or better yet, enroll in a course on computer-assisted diving.

In the final analysis, all computers do what they are designed to do quite well. If you use them according to the manufacturer's instructions and with common sense, they'll do the job safely. You should base your purchase decision on your needs and on the quality of service and training you'll receive, not on any theoretical factors such as the decompression model or how many tissue compartments it contains. It's probably not a good idea to purchase a dive computer second-hand or by mail order. Choose a reputable local dive store where you can discuss your needs with a qualified instructor or knowledgeable salesperson.

ies have shown repetitive dives beyond 80 feet—particularly with short surface intervals—to be very dangerous. Yet, while some have expressed concern over the E-E model, they do have a history of reliability and safety. In addition, some E-E devices—notably those using algorithms based on the work of Dr. A.A. Buhlmann—are the most conservative on the market. (They use extremely conservative M-values).

The second class of dive computers calculate the decompression status of the initial dive as E-E models do (shifting tissue control during shallow portions of the dive). The difference is they base surface outgassing not on the controlling compartment of the dive, but on a predetermined compartment to control offgasing, regardless of the controlling compartment at depth. In devices of this type, the controlling compartment is the 60-minute half-time. Research conducted by the Diving Science and Technology Corporation in developing PADI's Recreational Dive Planner is the rationale for using the 60-minute compartment.

In leaving the discussion of how computers work, it must be stressed that we are still a long way off from having the "ultimate algorithm." According to Dr. Bruce Wienke of the Advanced Computing Laboratory at the Los Alamos National Laboratory, and noted author on decompression issues, the ultimate algorithm would involve consideration for more than merely dissolved gas absorption and elimination. It should also take into account bubble nucleation theories and collision coalescence (how small bubble meet and join into one). While it's possible to construct such models, Wienke stresses, they are extremely complicated and would require the use of sophisticated supercomputers. Even using today's highest technology computers and equally advanced algorithms, as much as a full day or more of number crunching would be required for the computer to determine the solutions. We won't have these kinds of capabilities in the computers we carry underwater for quite some time.

COMPUTER-DEPENDENT VS. COMPUTER-ASSISTED DIVING

Not so long ago a friend of mine—a certified instructor—returned from a deep wreck dive to 120 feet. He had dived the wreck many times in the past, so, the dive itself wasn't remarkable. What was remarkable was that he had already made two prolonged shallow dives on a nearby reef that same morning. As an instructor, he was certainly aware that a deep dive should never follow a shallow dive. Curious to find out the reason he ignored a basic rule of decompression safety, I asked him why he would make such a deep repetitive dive. His reply: "My computer said it was okay." What, I wondered, would he have done if his computer had told him to jump off the roof?

The incident pointed out an increasingly common problem among divers: When faced with making decisions, knowledge and common sense often lose out to technology. Certainly, it's easier to read some numbers off a computer display than to think. Yet, the best computers on earth have yet to match the capabilities of the human brain. And no program in existence has the subtlety and sophistication of simple common sense. Turning on your computer shouldn't mean turning off your brain.

PHOTO 4-3

Dive with the assistance of a computer, but don't be dependent upon it. Blind faith in technology is always an invitation to disaster.

At issue is the difference between computer-*assisted* diving and computer-*dependent* diving. Dive computers can aid the decision-making process; they should never dictate it. Used properly they are excellent tools. If, however, we follow them blindly without regard to common sense, they can lull us into behavior that is both stupid and dangerous. My friend the instructor is an excellent example.

What Computers Can Do...and What They Can't

A lot of misconceptions surround dive computers, as an incident at a seminar a few years ago will illustrate. During the program, an engineer for a dive computer manufacturer told an enlightening story. He had received a letter from a diver who had bought his company's device. An experienced diver, she was very complimentary of the wrist-mounted model she used. But she expressed some serious reservations. She explained that a friend had purchased the same computer. Unlike her wrist-mounted device, his was a console-mounted model. This was the source of her concern, because in her letter she asked, "If my buddy doesn't wear the computer on his wrist, then how can it monitor his blood?" For an experienced diver to hold such an incredible misconception shows just how little many divers really understand about dive computers.

Let's begin by clarifying that dive computers are not blood-gas monitors. Like your digital wristwatch or hand-held calculator, they only "crunch numbers." Dive computers do not and cannot tell you what's actually happening inside your body. As you know now from reading Chapter Two, no one even knows for certain if there's any real physiological basis to any existing decompression model. What's programmed into the memory of a dive computer is nothing more than a mathematical prediction model. Assuming no unusual circumstances, these models normally work quite well. But, they are not infallible. They have no way of knowing, for example, if you are overweight, are engaging in strenuous exercise, or partied until four in the morning. In fact, even when used within the parameters called for by their designers, computers sometimes still can't prevent DCS. The same, of course, is true of dive tables.

Does this mean that dive computers are dangerous? Absolutely not. It means that, as with any form of technology, the information they provide should be only part of what goes into making a decision. To use dive computers wisely, you must follow a few guidelines, regardless of what the information tells you in the display.

GUIDELINES FOR SAFE COMPUTER USE

1. Follow the manufacturer's instructions: Proper computer use begins with familiarizing yourself with the manufacturer's instructions and recommendations. These instructions—contained in the owner's manual—will explain how to operate the computer. Some devices, for example, have on/off switches. Others activate automatically. You will also learn what information the computer will provide, how to read the display and what circumstances are beyond its capabilities. (While all dive computers handle no-decompression diving, they vary greatly in how they handle decompression diving.)

2. Your tissues must be "clean" before using a computer: When you turn a dive computer on (*initialize*, in computer jargon), it assumes that you have not made any previous dives. If you have made a dive, you should wait at least 18 to 24 hours for the nitrogen level in your body to return to normal before using a dive computer.

3. Be careful about loaning your computer: After making a dive using a computer, that device cannot be used by another diver—unless it is

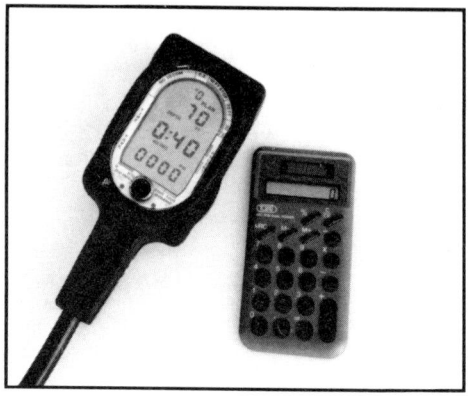

PHOTO 4-4

A dive computer isn't a panacea for decompression sickness. Like any calculator, they do nothing more than "crunch numbers."

reinitialized. How you reinitialize a computer varies according to the model. Devices equipped with on/off switches are reinitialized when they are turned off and then on again. Others provide a magnet that, when placed over the display, erases all memory of previous dives. Once activated, some computers cannot be reinitialized. This is to prevent accidentally turning off the device and losing all the data. While this design feature makes the computer foolproof, it also prevents its use by another diver until it has completed its outgassing calculations.

4. Buddies should never share a computer: One of the most potentially dangerous practices is sharing a single computer among a buddy team. No matter how conscientious divers are about staying together, buddies never dive the exact same profile. This means only the buddy wearing the computer will get valid data on his decompression status. Either both buddies should wear their own computer, or you must plan the dive using dive tables. There are no other safe alternatives. Incidentally, by basing the dive plan on the most conservative device, you can build an extra measure of safety into the dive.

5. Never turn your computer off if you expect to make a repetitive dive: For you to be able to make a repetitive dive, your computer must retain all information from previous dives within a certain period.

If you turn it off by mistake, all memory of previous dives is lost, and the computer cannot be used for repetitive diving. (As noted before, some computers prevent this problem by not having an on/off switch so the device cannot be turned off once initialized.) Exactly what constitutes a repetitive dive varies according to the model you use. Some devices assume you are completely outgassed in as little as six hours. Other models assume outgassing can take 48 hours or longer.

6. Avoid diving to limits: The worst example of abandoning common sense for technology is continuing a dive until the no-decompression limit is at or near zero. This is sometimes called "riding the zero" and can be an extremely dangerous practice. When you're diving below 80 feet, always begin your ascent—either to the surface or a shallower depth—while the display shows at least 3 to 5 minutes remaining . When diving above 80 feet, begin your ascent with at least 10 minutes remaining. What we know about decompression sickness is far from complete. Diving to a computer's limits is like a test pilot "pushing the envelope" on a new aircraft design: It might work, but then again, it might not. The consequences of the wrong outcome are far too great to risk a few more minutes of bottom time.

If you do accidentally exceed a no-decompression limit, your computer will give you information on the depth and time for a decompression stop. Unlike a safety stop, this is a requirement, not a suggestion. After decompressing, you should remain out of the water for at least 12 hours before making another dive—regardless of what your computer tells you.

7. Ascend at the proper rate: The ascent rates programmed into computers vary according to the model you use. They range from 60 feet to less than 30 feet per minute. Whatever the rate specified for your device, it's very important that you not exceed it (slower is okay). One of the many benefits of using a computer is its ability to function as an ascent rate indicator. Should you exceed the specified ascent rate, the display will flash, or you will hear an audible beep, warning you to slow down. Learn to be attentive to this valuable safety feature.

8. Always make a safety stop: Safety stops are among the best measures to prevent decompression sickness. Halting your ascent for 3 to 5 minutes at a depth between 10 and 20 feet allows nitrogen in the faster compartments to release more efficiently. The stop also slows your ascent rate. On multilevel profiles, an even better practice is to complete the final portion of your dive in water 20 feet or less. This allows you to continue to enjoy the dive rather than just blowing bubbles in mid-water. Safety stops are doubly important on dives below 60 feet or on any dive where you are within 5 minutes of a no-decompression limit. We'll discuss more about safety stops in Chapter Five.

9. Avoid deep repetitive dives: Most divers know their deepest dive of the day should be their first. Statistically, deep repetitive dives account for a significant percentage of DCS incidents. To avoid being one of these statistics, limit all repetitive dives to 80 feet or less—regardless of what your computer says you can do.

10. Avoid decompression dives: Some dive computers are very sophisticated. They will give you your decompression status far beyond the no-decompression limits. But, even though some devices will let you make decompression dives, the best advise is don't do it. Decompression diving is extremely dangerous. It requires extensive planning and support. In fact, it violates the very definition of "recreational diving" (no-stop diving, no deeper than 130 feet). Even taking the appropriate precautions won't eliminate a higher-than-normal risk of DCS compared with no-stop diving. Many researchers believe that the popular models used today to predict no-stop diving are inadequate for predicting profiles requiring stops. While others disagree, the point is nobody knows for sure. All that is certain is that statistically the risk of DCS increases significantly when you exceed no-stop limits. Until we learn more about why this happens, it's foolish to risk your health merely for more time under water.

11. Know what to do if your computer fails: If your computer should fail during a dive, terminate the dive immediately and follow the manufacturer's instructions in the owner's manual. If you don't remember the instructions, begin an immediate ascent, making a safety stop for at least 10 minutes at 10 to 20 feet before surfacing. If your computer fails during a surface interval, you could continue to dive provided you don't exceed a depth of 25 feet.

You might also be able to make a single repetitive dive deeper than 25 feet. Here's how it works: While on the surface, the computer will go into "scroll mode" and read out a series of depths and adjusted no-decompression limits. Get in the habit of recording this data in your logbook. Then, if the device fails, you'll have the information to make a second dive deeper than 25 feet. A third repetitive dive deeper than 25 feet will, of course, not be possible. Remain out of the water for at least 12 hours when switching from a computer to dive tables.

12. Know when it's safe to fly: With the increasing popularity of dive computers, there is special concern over the flying-after-diving issue. Generally, dive computers handle flying after diving in one of two ways. Some devices do not indicate a waiting period before flying. Instead, they defer to industry guidelines such as the DAN recommendation detailed on page 102. Others provide specific indications of when flying is permitted.

The problem is that some devices suggest far less time before flying than the DAN guideline. Some contend that this reduced time interval is reasonable because the computer is basing its calculations on your specific dive profile, not a recommendation for all divers. Until we know more about the silent bubble phenomenon, and computer models are refined to deal with the intricacies of flying after diving, it's best to be conservative. Many advise that dive computer users abide by either the current DAN guideline or the computer, whichever is the more conservative.

SOME PARTING THOUGHTS

Experts in the field of diving physiology disagree on what's the best decompression model. But most agree the decompression phenomenon is probably far more complex than current models assume. Science also knows that no existing model can predict the avoidance of DCS with 100-percent certainty. Some dives even within a model sometimes result in DCS.

Yet, these models are what designers program into the memory of dive computers. The conclusion is that we are nowhere near the point at which we can depend on technology alone for our safety. All we can really count on to take care of us is our own intelligence and common sense. Use technology, but use it wisely. Remember, you need two computers to dive safely—the one on your wrist and the one between your ears.

CHAPTER FIVE

The Recipe for Absolute Safety— Don't Dive!

Reducing the Risk of DCS

While theoretical discussions of decompression sickness may be interesting, it's how we put this information into practice that makes us safer divers. That's the purpose of this chapter—turning theory into practice. A lot of misunderstanding and controversy surround many of the issues we'll discuss. And much of what isn't controversial is clouded by scientific uncertainty. By sorting through the facts, opinions, and misconceptions, however, you should get a better understanding of these issues and be able to turn knowledge into action.

The first section will explore two simple yet important techniques—ascent rates and safety stops. We'll examine why and how you should avoid high-risk diving practices such as bounce dives and reverse and sawtooth profiles, along with the impact snorkeling has on bends risk. We'll offer advice on how to maximize safety when making multiday repetitive dives. And we'll take an in-depth look at reducing the risk of DCS when you combine diving with flying or simply driving to altitude.

ASCENT RATES

A common misconception among divers is that you must exceed the no-decompression limit to make a decompression dive. Actually, whether you exceed the limit or not, every dive is a decompression dive. Even if you don't make a decompression stop, your body must still slowly offgas excess nitrogen as you return to the surface. This makes your ascent a form of decompression; and the rate of decompression is controlled by how fast you ascend.

Evolution of Ascent Rates

Early in your diver training you probably learned to ascend no faster than 60 feet per minute (fpm). Many have assumed this rate, like holy script, is immutable—at least until recently. A question often asked by divers is, "How did they come up with this particular rate?" The story behind the 60-fpm rate illustrates that many supposedly unalterable rules have been determined in less-than-scientific ways.

According to Dr. Edward Lanphier, a former U.S. Navy medical officer, when the Royal Navy adopted Haldane's decompression tables, it implemented an ascent rate of 60 fpm to avoid hauling the diver up past his first decompression stop. (Haldane's original tables did not have a specific ascent rate, only total time for ascent, which included decompression time.)

When the U.S. Navy adopted the Royal Navy tables with little change, it too instituted the 60-fpm rule, so it became the ascent rate specified back in 1916 for the original U.S. Navy Bureau of Construction Tables. Somehow, for reasons never explained, The *USN Diving Manual* of 1943 changed this rate to 25 fpm.

In the mid-1950s when the "new" U.S. Navy Tables were under development, the ascent rate was a matter of some dispute between the Navy's "deep-sea" divers and its new "frogmen" (scuba divers). The deep-sea contingent wanted the then-current 25-fpm standard retained, because it was a comfortable rate at which to haul up a surface-supplied diver. The scuba-diving contingent objected, saying this was an impossibly slow rate of ascent for a free-swimming diver. They advocated a 100 fpm rate. As a practical human compromise—having no particular scientific basis—the group settled for 60 fpm. It has been with us ever since.

With the development of the Doppler Bubble Detector in the 1970s, scientists conducted several studies of the Navy Tables. Each found a high incidence of asymptomatic or "silent bubbles" present in divers after surfacing from dives defined as no-decompression. Alarmed by these results, some researchers advocated slowing the decompression rate by slowing the ascent rate. This, they reasoned, would reduce silent bubbling and—they hoped—the probability of DCS. Satisfied, however, with the performance of its tables in preventing DCS, the Navy did not see any need to amend the 60-fpm ascent rate.

A Divergence of Opinion

With the introduction of modern microprocessor-based dive computers in the early 1980s, the ascent-rate issue was thrown once more into the spotlight. Following the advice of earlier dive-table studies, many manufacturers opted for reduced ascent rates—some as slow as 30 fpm. Others prescribed a variable ascent rate dependent upon depth. The closer the diver got to the surface, the slower the ascent rate. Still other manufacturers stood by the old standard of 60 feet per minute.

One of the primary advocates of maintaining the 60-fpm standard was dive computer engineer Dr. John Lewis. Using a computer model with 1,500 tissue compartments, Lewis made a convincing argument that 60 fpm was an adequate ascent rate. With his model, he has shown that slowing the ascent rate has little impact on reducing nitrogen pressures in tissue compartments.

While Lewis may be correct about the minimal impact a slowed ascent rate has on decompression safety, it is not the only consideration. Decompression is only one of the problems facing the diver on ascent. The other is lung overexpansion. But just how could a slower ascent be helpful here?

Practical experience with more than 30 years of scuba diving, coupled with the best medical evidence, indicates that humans can tolerate a 60-fpm ascent rate without risking lung overexpansion.

FIGURE 5-1

Moderating your ascent rate—no faster than 60 fpm—and taking a safety stop are two of the most important steps you can take in reducing your risk of DCS.

This assumes the diver is breathing properly, has no other history of lung disease, and is actually ascending at the proper rate. This last assumption is where theory and practice begin to diverge.

A simple observation on your next dive should confirm to you that divers quite often ascend faster than 60 fpm. In fact, unless they have a mechanical aid, divers usually have little idea of how fast they ascend. Probably the only controlled study of ascent rates, conducted in the 1970s by Dr. Glen Egstrom at UCLA, showed the average ascent rate among sport divers was between 120 and 160 fpm. The conclusion is that the problem isn't the 60-fpm ascent rate; the problem is that divers regularly exceed this rate, and often by substantial margins. Advocating a rate of less than 60 fpm, therefore, might be a way of getting divers to reduce their actual ascent rate to at least 60 fpm. Another method is to use a mechanical device to gauge the ascent rate. As all dive computers have an ascent-rate monitor, this becomes an important benefit of computer-assisted diving.

So what's the final word on ascent rates? As in most issues involving DCS, no one knows for sure. On one hand, little empirical evidence exists to justify an ascent rate slower than 60 fpm as a way of increasing decompression safety. From a practical standpoint, however, we cannot ignore that divers often ascend at rates far greater than 60 fpm. The best advice is to follow one of two practices:

(1) If you don't use a computer, try to develop both the awareness and skill to ascend at a rate slower than 60 fpm. This way, even if you exceed your normal rate, you'll still probably not exceed 60 fpm.

(2) The better option is to use a dive computer and pay careful attention to the ascent-rate indicator. Your ascent rate is a lot like a speed limit on the highway. You can get away with going slower than the limit. But, you'll eventually pay the price for going over it.

SAFETY STOPS

While there's controversy over the value of reduced ascent rates, there's agreement on the value of safety stops. As this is sometimes a confusing issue, let's begin by looking at the difference between a safety stop and a decompression stop.

A decompression stop is a required delay in the diver's ascent before surfacing. This occurs when the diver exceeds the no-decompression limit provided in the decompression model (table or computer) he is using. Without such a stop, the diver will exceed the maximum allowable nitrogen level in one or more of his tissue compartments, making DCS a likely outcome (though not a certainty).

Conversely, decompression models do not require safety stops. A safety stop is merely a way of incorporating an added margin of protection. By delaying the ascent, a diver accomplishes a slower and safer elimination of nitrogen than ascending immediately to the surface.

Technically, a diver could opt not to make a safety stop—ascend directly to the surface—and not violate the decompression model. There are, however, compelling reasons to make safety stops.

The Evidence

For those who like facts to back up advice, none is more convincing than a study conducted several years ago at the University of Southern California's Catalina Marine Science Center exploring how safety stops could affect silent bubbling. The hypothesis was that safety stops could reduce silent bubbles; and a test was set up where volunteer scuba divers dove to 100 feet for 25 minutes (the no-decompression limit of the U.S. Navy Tables). One group of divers ascended directly to the surface. Another group made a two-minute stop at 10 feet before surfacing. Still a third group stopped for one minute at 20 feet and then four minutes at 10 feet before surfacing. All divers were monitored for silent bubbles for two hours after surfacing.

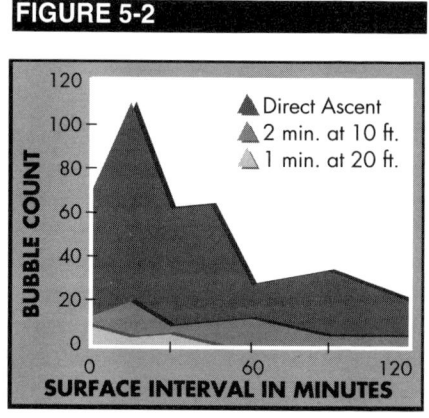

FIGURE 5-2

The results are summarized in *Figure 5-2*. Note the high incidence of silent bubbles in the no-stop group. Even more striking is that the one-stop group drastically reduced its silent bubbles, and the two-stop group almost completely eliminated them. If you accept that a relationship exists between silent bubbles and DCS—as do most diving medical experts—no more evidence should be necessary to convince you of the value of safety stops.

Safety stops are important for another reason—they make you think about your ascent. This is something many of us simply don't do.

When the time comes to ascend, it's common to head for the surface oblivious to the ascent rate. If you plan to make a safety stop, however, you are unlikely to ascend so thoughtlessly. By planning to stop before surfacing you must ascend in a controlled, deliberate manner. This gives you an added benefit as you approach shallow water.

Your safety stop should take place at a depth of from 10 to 20 feet. If you remember back to your entry-level course, the greatest change in volume in a flexible, air-filled container—like your lungs—occurs between two atmospheres (33 feet) and one atmosphere (the surface). So, the greatest danger from a lung overexpansion injury is in shallow water. Your rate of ascent—particularly in shallow water—then becomes an important factor not only in avoiding DCS, but lung over-expansion, too. Even if you are breathing normally, shutting off your airway by an innocuous action such as swallowing, combined with a rapid rate of ascent, could result in a lung overexpansion injury. Slowing your ascent as you approach the surface reduces the likelihood of such an accident.

How to Make a Safety Stop

Assuming you're now convinced of the need for safety stops, the next issue is understanding what circumstances warrant making a stop, and how to do it properly. First, nothing is wrong with making a safety stop after every dive. Planning a stop as part of every dive helps you maintain your neutral buoyancy skills, and makes you more aware of your ascent rate. If, however, you wish to limit your safety stops to situations when they are most important in avoiding DCS, the advice is simple: You should make a safety stop at the end of any dive deeper than 60 feet or anytime you dive to or near (within about 3 to 5 minutes) the no-decompression limit.

What follows are some guidelines for making an effective safety stop. You should practice these techniques as part of every ascent. That way, you'll develop good diving habits, and the procedures will become second nature.

1. Never take the elevator: A proper safety stop begins as you leave the bottom. Many divers get into a bad habit of adding air to their BCD when they ascend and using this positive buoyancy to "take the elevator" to the surface. You should never do this. A positively buoyancy ascent is not a controlled ascent. Some air in your BCD can help offset the effect of excessive negative buoyancy at depth. But, the effort of kicking is what should dictate the speed of your ascent. Your buoyancy is correct only if you stop ascending when you stop kicking. If you don't stop when you quit kicking, you should let some air out of your BCD.

2. Ascend hand-over-hand when possible: You'll often have a rope or line to aid your ascent, particularly if you're diving from a boat. If you do have an ascent line, use it. Ascending hand-over-hand on a line, without kicking, is an excellent way to control your ascent rate and conserve energy. It also helps avoid kicking the mask off any diver below you. When in rough seas, however, be careful when using the anchor line of a boat. Severe pitching of the boat can make the anchor line difficult or even dangerous to handle. It could also pull you up several feet through the water at a rapid, uncontrolled rate.

Making a safety stop requires good buoyancy control skills and paying attention to your depth. Practice these techniques often.

3. Practice your ascent rate often: Learning what a proper ascent rate should feel like can be difficult. A good way to judge this is by using a mechanical aid. Practice ascending at the proper rate with a computer or ascent-rate indicator. Then, without the device, have your buddy time you in an unaided ascent. Continue practicing until the proper rate becomes second nature.

Another way of judging your ascent is simply to take the depth into account. Your ascent rate should be no faster than 60 fpm, or 1 foot per second. It should, therefore, take you at least the same number of seconds to reach the surface as the depth from which you began the ascent (ideally, a little longer).

4. Delete all air from your BCD before reaching 20 feet: Too much air in your vest sometimes makes it difficult to halt your ascent as you reach shallow water. Prepare to stop by letting out air from your BCD (buoyance compensator device) as you near the surface. By the time you reach 20 feet, you should have little if any air left in your BCD. Once at your safety stop, you can add a small amount of air to offset any negative buoyancy.

5. Practice "hovering" often: You will not always have the aid of an ascent line to help you. When you don't, you'll have to maintain your position at the safety stop using only your buoyancy control skills. This is where "hovering" becomes an essential skill. Hovering is the ability to remain absolutely motionless in mid-water by using your BCD and breathing patterns. If you can't hover well, the struggle to maintain your position can cause you to exert a lot of energy. Heavy physical exertion could interfere with the normal elimination of nitrogen and subject you to an increased risk of DCS. Relax and avoid exertion while at your safety stop.

6. Be careful to maintain your depth: Safety stops should take place in a depth range of 10 to 20 feet. But maintaining a precise depth can be difficult in open water when the sea state is anything but calm. In controlling your depth, tend toward the deeper end of the range. Getting deeper in the water column makes you less subject to the effects of surge and gives you a margin of error in case you begin to ascend inadvertently. It also helps you avoid being hit by boats that might pass overhead. Keep a constant eye on your depth gauge to make sure you're not slowly descending or ascending.

7. Remain at the stop for an appropriate amount of time: The general recommendation is to spend at least three to five minutes at the safety stop. Some authorities, however, suggest that you remain at the safety stop for either three to five minutes or a period equal to ten percent of the bottom time of the dive—whichever is greater. The point is, you can't spend too long at a safety stop.

8. Forget the "be back with 500 psi" rule: It's common to plan your dive so you're back on shore—or on board the boat—with at least 500 psi of air remaining. The purpose of this rule is to avoid running out of air while at depth and to save enough air to return to the exit point. Actually, hurrying out of the water to save a certain amount of air isn't helpful. Instead, amend the rule to: Plan your dive so you are at your safety stop with no less than 500 psi. It's better to exit the water with no air remaining after making a safety stop than to exit with 500 psi having made no safety stop. The air that's left in your tank can't help you avoid DCS.

AVOIDING HIGH-RISK PRACTICES

Although it's unclear exactly why, researchers and those who treat bent divers know that certain practices put some divers at a higher risk of getting DCS than others. These practices include various types of dive profiles and making numerous repetitive dives over several days. Even snorkeling may have some impact on DCS.

Problematic Profiles

Reverse Profiles: A reverse profile is a multilevel dive that starts in shallow water and ends in deep. The term is also used to describe the practice of making a deep repetitive dive after a shallow dive. Avoid these situations at all costs. Always begin a multilevel dive at the deepest point of the profile, and ascend to gradually decreasing depths. Finishing a dive during the deeper part of a profile is also more dangerous should an out-of-air emergency occur.

Sawtooth Profiles: As the name implies, a "sawtooth" profile is a dive where you continually alter your depth. Avoid constantly ascending and descending, and try to stay within a consistent depth range. Also, plan your dive so you don't have to ascend to check the location of the dive boat or exit point. Maintain your orientation by learning to use your compass and detect clues from the underwater terrain. When multilevel diving, once you have ascended to a shallower portion of the profile, never return to a deeper depth.

Bounce Dives: Bounce dives are short, deep dives made after a previous dive to any depth. Many of us have seen—or are guilty ourselves of making—the classic bounce dive. It usually starts as "just a quick dive to retrieve the anchor." Often, these "quickie dives" result in yet another dive—one in a recompression chamber.

Multiday, Repetitive Diving: A Word to the Wise

The most important benefit of dive computers is that they allow you to dive longer and more often. But, as with all good things, this comes with a price. No decompression model so far—and thus no dive computer—was designed and tested conclusively for multiple day, multiple dive use. Yet, this is exactly the kind of diving sport divers do—particularly while vacationing at dive resorts. Statistical evidence from the Divers Alert Network suggests that the divers at highest risk for DCS

PHOTO 5-2

Be extra careful when making several dives over several days, such as when you're on vacation. Take a day off from diving toward the middle of your trip, or at least ease up on the number of dives you're making toward the end.

are those who make multiday, repetitive dives.

To reduce your risk, DAN recommends either of two common-sense suggestions. One is to curtail diving toward the end of the trip. The second is to take a day off to go sightseeing or just lay on the beach in the middle of your trip. Either practice will help reduce your nitrogen levels and, hopefully, your risk of DCS on a diving vacation. You should also limit the depth of any repetitive dive to a maximum of 80 feet. Dives deeper than 80 feet should be confined to the first dive of the day.

Snorkeling and DCS

Can a snorkeler get the bends? The short answer is, yes. DCS has been seen in the Ama pearl divers of Japan and Korea, and others who engage in deep free diving over periods of days or years. DCS-like symptoms are also seen among free divers in Polynesia. There, in the course of studying more than 200 divers, one researcher documented almost 50 cases of what the islanders call *taravana*, which translates as "fall crazy." Symptoms included extreme vertigo, nausea, temporary unconsciousness, paralysis and even two cases of death. The world-famous Cuban free diver Francisco "Pipin" Ferreras maintains that he's been bent twice after spearfishing at depths in excess of 150 feet. (Pipin holds the world free-diving record of 410 feet.)

While this may be an interesting aside, the average—or even above average—recreational snorkeler hasn't much to worry about as far as getting DCS. Given the modest depths and times of the average free diver, the gas absorbed is just too little to make any difference.

The more important question is what impact snorkeling might have when it's done between repetitive scuba dives. It probably has a lot to do with what you consider "snorkeling." Lying on the surface of the water, or leisurely diving down to 10 to 20 feet periodically, is unlikely to cause any problem. If, on the other hand, you mean aggressive free diving, where you're making multiple trips to considerable depths, then that could mean something else entirely.

At issue is the effect of vigorous exercise after diving. Most authorities caution against it because of how it changes circulatory dynamics and offgassing rates. But as discussed in Chapter One, such warnings are based on speculation rather than empirical evidence. The best advice is to limit your snorkeling between repetitive dives to paddling around with your face in the water watching the pretty fish below you. The continual ascending and descending of skin diving probably doesn't help the outgassing process much, either. Until we know more about decompression, divers are wise to avoid heavy exertion—including vigorous snorkeling—between or after diving.

THE SECOND ASCENT: FLYING AFTER DIVING

As a diver, you know that when you surface after a dive your nitrogen levels do not immediately return to normal. Excess or residual nitrogen remains in your body for several hours—even days—after diving. Only gradually does this higher level return to its pre-dive state. Importantly, even though the nitrogen level isn't back to normal, it's still within a "tolerable limit," as defined by the dive tables. The dive tables, however, make one important assumption: that, upon surfacing, you return to an ambient pressure of 1 atmosphere, or 14.7 psi.

When we fly in an airplane or drive through the mountains after diving, it's like making two ascents: the first to the surface, and the second to a pressure of less than 1 atm. The problem is that the decreased pressure negates the entire premise of standard dives tables and may result in exceeding the "tolerable limits" of the residual nitrogen.

This situation doesn't mean that we can never fly nor drive to altitude after diving. It does, however, require that we follow special procedures to take the "second ascent" into account. But before we explore the current recommendations and other pertinent issues, let's look first at how flying after diving procedures evolved.

History of Procedures

One of the first flying-after-diving guidelines embraced by recreational divers was the National Oceanic and Atmospheric Administration (NOAA) "Group D rule." The rule stated that flying was safe up to a maximum altitude of 8,000 feet/2,400 meters as long as the diver was in Repetitive Group D or lower (according to the U.S. Navy Tables). While this guideline was consistent with the mathematics of the U.S. Navy tables, practical experience showed that it wasn't always conservative enough. One researcher, for example, documented almost 50 cases of DCS where divers were within Group D or lower.

Somewhat later the National Aeronautics and Space Administration (NASA) proposed a new rule allowing for flight up to 8,000 feet after a two hour waiting period, regardless of the Repetitive Group Designation. The diver could not exceed the U.S. Navy no-decompression limits, and could make only a single, non-repetitive dive. This made it of dubious value for recreational divers. Furthermore, while the rule was in keeping with the mathematics of the U.S. Navy Tables, some studies documented significant silent bubbling in divers following similar—and even more conservative—guidelines.

In 1982 the British Admiralty's Diving Advisory Committee adopted a new rule as a guideline for commercial divers working in the North Sea. Soon after, the recreational diving community embraced the guideline, and it became the industry standard in North America for many years. The recommendation was as follows: For no-decompression dives, with less than one hour spent at depth, it was safe to fly after a minimum wait of four hours. For all other situations a 12-hour wait was required. The problem was that these guidelines were not intended to address repetitive diving.

The story of the current recommendation for flying after diving begins in February 1989 at a workshop sponsored by the Undersea and Hyperbaric Medical Society (UHMS). The conference was convened to reach some scientifically based consensus applicable to all diving situations, including recreational diving. While much scientific theory existed to support the need for a revised guideline, little data existed involving actual cases of DCS after flying—at least in recreational divers. But what data were available indicated that, of those divers who were symptom-free before flying, symptoms usually occurred during a flight within 24 hours of their last dive.

Based on this data, the workshop participants recommended that divers wait 24 hours after diving before flying—especially after multiple dives over multiple days. For dives requiring decompression stops, they suggested a period of from 24 to 48 hours before flying.

While the participants may have drawn good working guidelines from the limited data they had, they failed to recognize what practical effect this would have for the recreational diving community— especially dive resorts. This guideline would mean curtailing all diving within 24 hours of a flight home, a serious restriction. Furthermore, the recommendation presented serious liability questions for dive operators. What, for example, were the liability implications for a resort that allowed guests to dive within this 24-hour period?

By late 1990, many in the recreational diving community began to question the basis of this recommendation, contending the data sample was far too small to draw a definitive conclusion. The UHMS emphasized that its statement was meant only as a suggestion, not a rule. But this did little to quell the concerns of the recreational community. Recognizing that any "suggestion" from such an important organization as the UHMS would certainly become an industry standard, the scientific community was asked to re-evaluate its position.

PHOTO 5-3

Make sure you're aware of the special concerns of combining flying with diving, and follow the current flying-after-diving guidelines.

At a UHMS conference in June 1991 a paper was presented reviewing 62 cases of DCS that occurred in divers after flying. These were all the cases reported to the Divers Alert Network from 1987 through 1990 in which the victim was symptom-free before flying. While the paper provided an interesting perspective on the problem, it was unable to answer the question of what these figures really meant in terms of the risk of getting DCS. What wasn't documented was the total population of divers who flew after diving. Without a valid population base number, there was no way to determine a measurable risk factor and, therefore, a verifiable guideline.

The conference did, however, assert that the current guideline might be overly restrictive to the general diving public and might place dive operators in an unjustified liability position. In the fall of 1991, based on the findings of the UHMS conference, the Divers Alert Network issued a flying-after-diving guideline that's been revised only slightly in the years since. (See page 102 for the most recent DAN recommendation.)

Environmental Considerations

The theoretical question of when it's safe to fly after diving is based on the same mathematical models used to develop dive tables. But, as we've seen in our examination of decompression theory, these models have their limitations. In particular, they are unable to take into account individual factors (such as age or obesity) and environmental factors (such as temperature or exertion).

Logically, you might assume that environmental factors play no part in the flying-after-diving issue. After all, the diver is in the safety and comfort of an aircraft cabin—a far cry from the stress of being under water. The truth is that while the environmental stresses placed on the human body are different in flying than in diving, the stress of flying can be as extreme and significant as diving.

Take, for example, the mere fact of being at altitude. At cruising altitude, cabin pressure in a modern jetliner is maintained at an equivalent pressure of at about 5,000-8,000 feet. The higher altitude means "thinner air" or less available oxygen. The result is that, even while sitting restfully in your seat, your body is working harder to deliver oxygen to your tissues than if you were at sea level. But altitude isn't the only factor causing stress.

In addition to less oxygen in the air you're breathing, there's also the quality of that air. In modern jetliners most of the air you breathe is recirculated. (60 percent or more, depending on the aircraft). This means that what you—along with 200 or 300 other passengers—breathe out, you will probably breathe back in again. Several studies have shown levels of bacteria and other contaminants 10 to 20 times that of normal air. While scientists debate the true risk of breathing cabin air, the fact is, yet another environmental stress is imposed on us. Finally, add to this the thousands of poisons present in continually recirculated cigarette smoke (on flights where smoking is allowed), and we have an environment that's less than ideal for healthy human functioning. For divers it's even worse—we're also concerned about any effects on the offgassing of nitrogen from our last dive. But there's even more.

DAN Flying-after-Diving Guidelines

1. Divers making single dives per diving day should have a minimum surface interval of 12 hours before ascending to altitude. This includes going to altitude by aircraft, automobile, or any other means.

2. Divers who make multiple dives per day or over many days, or dives that require obligated decompression stops, should take special precautions and wait for an extended surface interval beyond 12 hours before ascending to altitude. Extended surface intervals allow for additional denitrogenation and may reduce the likelihood of developing symptoms. For those diving heavily during an extended vacation, it may not be a bad idea to take a day off at midweek, or save the last day to buy souvenirs.

3. Remember: There can never be a flying-after-diving rule guaranteed to prevent decompression sickness, no matter how long the surface interval. Rather, research has produced this guideline that represents the best estimate for the majority of divers for a conservative, preflight surface interval. There will always be an occasional diver whose physiological makeup or unique diving circumstances will result in decompression sickness.

4. Know when you should say when.

Probably the most significant consideration involving cabin air is its low humidity. Because any air introduced from outside while at altitude is virtually free of humidity, the only source of moisture in cabin air is from the perspiration and exhaled breath of your fellow passengers. This, too, makes for a far less-than-healthy environment. The result is that our body must use its own fluid to rehydrate the air we breathe. Over time this causes dehydration. As we saw in the first chapter on the causes of decompression sickness, when we lose body fluids, our blood volume decreases, and even its biochemistry changes. This causes the blood to thicken or "sludge." The sludging causes decreased circulatory efficiency and inhibits the offgassing of nitrogen. The end result can be bubble formation or enlargement.

As circulatory efficiency decreases, symptoms of hypoxia can occur: fatigue, nausea, headache, and irritability. Interestingly, in at least one documented case, hypoxia has been so severe that the victim—a passenger who was a diver—mistakenly interpreted it as DCS. The bottom line is simple: Even under the best circumstances, an airliner cabin is not the best place for you to be while attempting to recover from the

Do's and Don'ts for Flying Divers

- Avoid dehydration by drinking lots of water—at least eight ounces per hour.
- Avoid alcohol and any drinks containing caffeine or sugar. Alcohol and caffeine cause you to lose fluid, and caffeine can actually change your heart rhythm. Sugar interferes with water absorption. Drink only water or unsweetened juice.
- Eat lightly before, during, and after flying. Eat meals containing 50-60 percent vegetables, grains, and fruits.
- Don't just sit there, do something! Get up and move around. Avoid staying in one position too long.
- Never, never, never smoke! It hurts both you and everyone else on board.

effects of a dive. (For some advice on what you can do to offset these effects, see "Do's and Don'ts for Flying Divers," above.)

Flying Before Diving

Some divers assume that flying *before* diving poses no problem. Others even insist that it imposes a safety factor because you start the dive with less nitrogen in your tissues than you would if you were saturated at sea-level pressure. In theory, this makes sense. In practice, however, it might lead you to a recompression chamber.

A diver arriving at a dive resort after several hours of flying is likely to be in far less than tip-top shape. The stresses of the cabin air, restricted circulation from sitting in a confined position, possible alcohol consumption, and general fatigue or nervousness from the journey are all factors that could place the diver under an increased—not decreased—risk for DCS. The best advice is to avoid diving until you are completely recovered and rested from the stress of your flight.

Driving to Altitude

A surprising number of divers never take into account that, to our bodies, altitude is altitude. It doesn't matter whether we get there in an aircraft or an automobile. This is of special concern to those of you who drive into mountains after diving at sea level.

Some divers take this situation into account by planning their sea-level dive as if it were at the altitude to which they'll be driving. Using altitude diving procedures, they reduce their dive times accordingly. While we again might have a situation where the theory says it's okay, practical experience says otherwise. Many researchers caution against this procedure because of the issue of silent bubbles. While it's likely that a shorter dive would produce fewer bubbles, that's not a certainty. If significant bubbles do form, then driving to altitude will aggravate the situation, just as if you got into an aircraft. The best advice is to treat any post-dive drive to altitude as if it were a flight and follow the appropriate guidelines.

SOME PARTING WORDS

For divers, DCS is a fact of life. Each year hundreds are stricken and seek treatment. But many more divers with mild symptoms ignore signs of DCS, or write it off as "just a strained muscle."

In most cases divers have no one to blame but themselves for getting DCS. Many incidents occur because divers simply ignore the dive tables or basic safety rules. Yet, even conscientious divers get bent. The conclusion is inescapable: Do anything you can to help reduce your risk. Don't exceed the ascent rate of your dive tables, take a safety stop at the end of every dive, avoid practices that could increase your risk, and be doubly conservative when flying before and especially after diving. Although not all cases of DCS can be prevented, a little knowledge and common sense can go a long way in reducing the risk.

CHAPTER SIX

Bent?...Nah, it's just a strained muscle.

Dealing with Decompression Sickness

In the previous chapters we've explored the proposed causes of decompression sickness, the numerous and insidious ways it can manifest itself, how dive tables and computers have evolved, and how to use them properly. We even provided some advice on how to minimize your risk of getting the bends. But, we have not yet addressed what you should do if it happens.

In this final chapter we'll explore the initial response and first aid for a DCS incident, including the role of oxygen and victim positioning. Next, we'll look at the definitive treatment for DCS—recompression—and see what's done once the victim arrives at a hyperbaric chamber. Finally, we'll close with an important but often overlooked examination of the psychological consequences of DCS.

FIRST AID MEASURES

The first step in any medical emergency is monitoring breathing, pulse, and the victim's level of consciousness. As shock can accompany any medical emergency, you should keep the victim warm and avoid any unnecessary movement.

For victims of decompression illness, there are also some special considerations. (In this chapter we'll use the term decompression illness or DCI instead of DCS because the first aid measures are the same regardless of whether you're dealing with lung expansion or supersaturation disorders.) To provide proper first aid to a DCI victim, you must first be able to recognize the symptoms. As we saw in Chapter One, symptoms are generally divided into the categories of mild or serious. To review, mild symptoms include extreme, unwarranted fatigue and itching, which are resolved by breathing pure oxygen. Serious symptoms are: pain, weakness, numbness/tingling, breathing difficulty, difficulty in seeing or hearing, alteration of speech, dizziness, nausea, or any level of decreased consciousness. If any of these symptoms occur after scuba diving—regardless of depth—you should assume some form of decompression illness, and begin the appropriate the first aid.

Victim Positioning

Generally, the immediate care for DCI is to administer pure oxygen while keeping the victim in the proper position. Let's first look at the issue of positioning before exploring the oxygen question.

For many years divers were taught to keep diving accident victims in the classic "feet up/head low position." (This is also known as the Trendelenburg Position.) While this might have some benefit for victims of arterial gas embolism (AGE), medical authorities have shown that it's of no value in the case of decompression sickness. In fact, the head-low position can cause breathing difficulty and other complications. Furthermore, it's often impossible for divers rendering first aid to distinguish the symptoms of AGE from decompression sickness, anyway. The lesson here is to treat all victims suspected of any form of DCI the same way.

Victim positioning does, however, depend on several factors. For a conscious victim displaying mild symptoms (extreme fatigue or itching), you should have him lay in a comfortable, horizontal position. Be certain to avoid any position that obstructs blood flow to an extremity, such as resting the head on an arm or crossing the legs. If possible, also have the victim drink four ounces of water or other nonalcoholic fluid every 15 minutes.

Due to the risk of lapsing into unconsciousness, the guideline for positioning victims of serious symptoms is a bit different than for those with mild symptoms. This is because unconscious or semi-conscious victims frequently vomit. So, they must lie in a position that reduces the likelihood of aspirating the vomitus or blocking the airway. In this case, use what's known as the *coma position*. This involves turning the

PHOTO 6-1

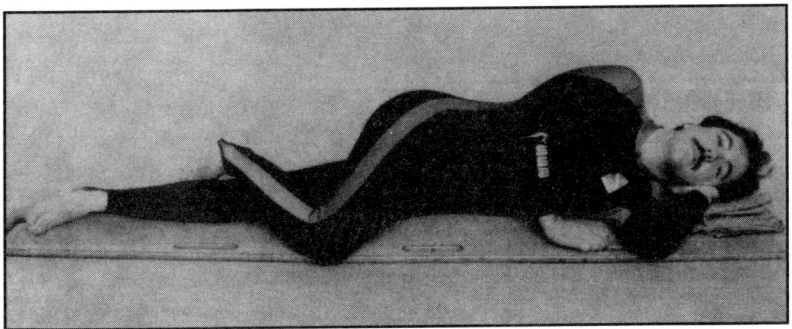

The coma position is advised for victims of serious DCI symptoms to reduce the likelihood of aspirating vomitus or blocking the airway should they become unconscious.

victim onto the left side, with the head supported at a low angle, and bending the upper leg at the knee to increase stability *[Photo 6-1]*. The coma position assists evacuating vomitus and helps keep the airway clear. Remember, however, a victim requiring CPR must lie flat on his back. Also, never administer liquids to anyone who is not completely conscious or who is suffering from stomach pain or urinal retention.

The Question of Oxygen

Once positioned properly, it's essential that the victim begin breathing pure oxygen. For maximum effect, it should be as close to a 100-percent concentration of oxygen as possible. Accomplishing this requires some understanding of oxygen delivery equipment. Small, disposable oxygen systems—such as those in your local drug store—are not designed to meet a person's full respiratory demand. Typically, these units provide a flow rate of about 6-10 liters per minute. (At rest a person need about 15-20 liters per minute.) Because they don't meet the full respiratory requirements, these systems come with masks that are vented. The vents allow ambient air to supplement the limited flow of oxygen. Unfortunately, this supplemental air dilutes the oxygen reaching the lungs to about 40 percent.

To obtain a 100-percent oxygen concentration, the DCI victim should breathe from a system that uses a demand valve—much like a scuba regulator—with a sealable mask. The demand valve design allows the oxygen system to meet the full respiratory demand of the victim. The mask, when sealed properly, prevents ambient air from reaching the victim. The result is an oxygen concentration of virtually 100 percent. (The mask should also be transparent so that vomiting is easier to detect.)

While learning to use oxygen systems is simple, it does require proper instruction. DAN and other organizations have set up Oxygen Provider courses for the general diving public. These courses usually last about four hours and include a review of

PHOTO 6-2

For maximum effectiveness an oxygen delivery system should include a demand valve regulator and transparent, sealable mask.

the causes and symptoms of DCI, along with practical sessions on how to set up and use oxygen delivery equipment. Any diver with current CPR certification is encouraged to enroll in one of these short, simple programs.

DEFINITIVE TREATMENT

First aid measures are only temporary. They are not a substitute for proper medical evacuation and treatment. Most often the treatment for DCI will include recompression at an appropriate facility. The effect of recompression is to reduce the size of the bubbles causing DCI. This, in turn, encourages the bubbles to diffuse into the surrounding tissues.

Another critical part of recompression therapy involves having the victim breathe pure oxygen at regular intervals. (Your body cannot tolerate breathing pure oxygen indefinitely.) This has numerous positive

PHOTO 6-3

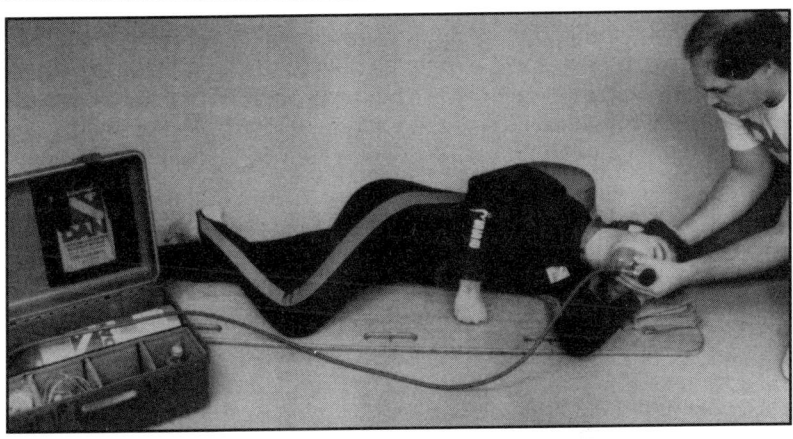

With proper training and the right equipment, administering oxygen to a DCI victim is easy. If you haven't already, consider taking an oxygen administration course.

effects which include accelerating the release of nitrogen, as well as increasing oxygenation and reducing swelling of the affected tissues.

Many divers are also unaware that during recompression, the victim normally receives aggressive drug therapy. Typically, intravenous fluids are administered to rehydrate the victim. Additionally, medications are given to reducing swelling in the brain and spinal cord and to counteract the changes in blood chemistry discussed in Chapter One.

The exact recompression schedule selected for a diving accident victim depends on whether the incident is decompression sickness or arterial gas embolism. Often, victims suspected of having decompression sickness undergo the "test of pressure" to help verify the working diagnosis. This involves recompression to 60 feet for 10 minutes while breathing pure oxygen. If this reduces or eliminates the symptoms, then the working diagnosis of DCS is confirmed, and a more extensive treatment regimen begins. If symptoms do not improve, then the diagnosis is questioned, but treatment often continues just in case bubbles are present. (For cases of suspected arterial gas embolism, the victim is recompressed to 165 feet to further reduce the size of any bubbles.)

Several treatment tables can be used for recompression therapy, but the ones most North American divers are likely to encounter were orig-

The Five-Minute Neurolgical Exam

Neurological symptoms of DCI are often very subtle. In fact, the victim himself may be unaware of certain symptoms unless a more thorough examination is conducted. What follows is a simple neurological assessment from DAN's *Underwater Diving Accident and Oxygen First Aid Manual*. Anyone can use it to determine the nature and extent of DCI symptoms. Be sure to write down the results and send them with the victim.

Orientation
Ask the diver if he knows his name and age; present location; time, day, or year.

Eyes
Have diver count number of fingers you display using both eyes together, then separately. Have him identify a distant object. While holding his head still, have diver follow the motion of your hand with his eyes only. Move your hand both up and down and side to side. Confirm that diver's eyes follow motion and do not jerk to one side and return. Also determine if pupils are equal in size.

Face
Ask diver to whistle. Determine if both sides of face have same expression while whistling. Have diver grit teeth and confirm by feel that jaw muscles are contracted equally. Have diver close his eyes while you touch his face and forehead. Confirm that sensation is present at each point of contact.

Hearing
Rub your thumb and forefinger together at a distance of about two feet from the diver's ear. Move your hand closer until diver can hear sound. Note distance from ear, and repeat procedure on other ear. Compare distance with your own hearing.

Swallowing Reflex
Have the diver swallow while you observe his "Adam's apple." Confirm that it moves up and down.

Tongue
Have the diver stick out his tongue. Confirm that it comes out straight and does not deviate to one side or the other.

Muscle Strength
Have the diver shrug shoulders while you bear down on them. Confirm equal muscle strength. Have him raise elbows to shoulder-level, and touch his chest with his hands. Instruct him to resist while you pull hands away from chest, push them back, then up and down. Strength should be approximately equal with both arms in all directions. Confirm leg strength by having diver lie down and raise and lower legs while you resist movement.

Sensory Perception
Instruct diver to close eyes. Starting at the head, lightly touch each side moving downward over entire length of body. Have diver confirm sensation.

Balance and Coordination
If not on a rocking boat, have diver stand with feet together, eyes closed and arms stretched out to his side. Be prepared to catch diver if he can't maintain balance. Check coordination by having diver alternately touch his nose and your finger held about 18 inches from his face. Next, with the diver lying down, have him slide the heel of one foot down the shin of the other leg. Check both sides and observe for unusual clumsiness on either side.

If you cannot perform all tests, give priority to Orientation, Muscle Strength, and Balance/Coordination. Record any omitted tests and reasons. Repeat tests at frequent intervals and note changes. Report all results to emergency response personnel.

inally developed by the U.S. Navy. Like other treatment regimes, these standard treatment tables are used as a guideline by medical personnel who modify them according to circumstances and the victim's response to treatment. Initial treatment often involves a descent to 60 feet for five or more hours in the cramped, noisy confines of a recompression chamber.

Unfortunately, it's not uncommon for the victim to require more than one treatment session. This less-than-successful outcome occurs especially when treatment is delayed or the victim does not begin breathing pure oxygen as soon as symptoms are noticed. For this reason, never delay in providing oxygen to anyone suspected of suffering from DCI; and always have an adequate supply of oxygen available along with the appropriate delivery system and trained personnel to administer it.

Furthermore, diving accident victims sometimes relapse or find that their symptoms are only partially resolved. In this case, follow-up treatments are administered, usually in 12- to 24-hour intervals. These sessions may last as long, or longer, than the original session.

PSYCHOLOGICAL CONSEQUENCES

While DCI is essentially a physiological disorder, it also has important psychological consequences. Dealing with decompression illness therefore means not only treating what's wrong inside the victim's body, but also helping the victim deal with what's going on inside his head, especially if he feels the illness is undeserved.

Many authorities describe a bends incident as either a "deserved hit" or an "undeserved hit." A deserved hit is a case of DCI where the victim obviously violated the tables or safety procedures. An undeserved hit is one where the diver followed all the rules but still fell victim. In this latter case particularly, the psychological consequences of the event can have a significant impact on the victim's mental and physical heath. The victim of an undeserved hit often feels that his body somehow "betrayed him." After all, he did nothing wrong. But if he doesn't resolve this conflict, it can lead to depression and perhaps other serious mental disorders.

To avoid negative psychological consequences, you should encourage the victim to talk about his feelings. In the case of a deserved hit, often the diver wants to use his experience as an object lesson to help others avoid the same mistake. This is an especially powerful desire

FIGURE 6-1

Therapy for DCI may not end with treatment in a recompression chamber. Psychological consequences are also common, particularly in cases of "undeserved hits."

among victims who are dive instructors. Encourage this desire, and don't just sweep the incident under the rug. In addition to the practical benefit in educating other divers, there's a therapeutic role in letting the victim put some positive meaning into an event that he may feel was a mistake.

Equally important, if it's an undeserved hit, you should make the victim understand that not all cases of bends are preventable. From what you have learned in the previous chapters, you can now appreciate the imprecise and poorly understood nature of the decompression phenomenon. The only way, in fact, to avoid DCI with complete certainty is never to dive. Virtually any dive exposes a diver to some risk of getting bent, even if he follows every rule and safety precaution to the letter. Unfortunately, some things in life just happen, and the bends is, at times, one of them.

Another important aspect of the psychology of DCI is how others react to bends victims. Much like the victims of many social diseases, divers who get bent are often stigmatized. They are ridiculed and reproached by their friends, diving professionals, and even, at times, the medical community. The inference is that they did something "wrong" or otherwise they wouldn't have gotten bent.

Dr. Jennifer Hunt of New York University Medical Center has done compelling and significant research into the social and psychological consequences of DCI. She points out several significant negative consequences of making value judgments on DCI victims. Moralizing serves no useful purpose; and chastising a bends victim only encourages him to hide his symptoms, or make him even more reluctant to seek treatment. If he does seek treatment, the fear of being branded "bad" or "wrong" makes it likely he will omit details about his profile or other information that could be vital to a proper diagnosis and resolution. The result could be not just psychological scars, but permanent physical damage from delayed or improper treatment. Dr. Hunt remarks, "In the face of social assault, divers are encouraged to maintain defenses such as denial and self-recrimination, which may minimize some immediate danger but can compromise their long-term psychological welfare."

Summarizing her research, Hunt goes on to emphasize, "DCI is not a moral disease and should not be treated as one. To do so damages the victim's chance at full physical and psychological recovery and has a negative impact on the diving community. This recognition does not constitute an acceptance of practices that some segments of the dive community feel put divers at risk. It simply acknowledges than divers who are bent suffer a serious physical illness than can have far-reaching consequences. Victims of decompression illness deserve understanding and treatment rather than social ridicule."

Diving Accident First Aid Procedures

1. Administer CPR if required, with victim lying flat (supine).
2. Keep airway open and prevent aspiration of vomitus. Unconscious victims should be intubated by trained personnel.
3. Administer oxygen by tight-fitting, transparent, double-seal mask at the highest possible oxygen concentration. Do not remove oxygen except to re-open the airway or if victim shows signs of convulsions.
4. Keep victim in the horizontal left-side-down position if symptoms occurred within ten minutes of surfacing and steps 1 through 3 have been completed.
5. If convulsion occurs, do not forcefully restrain. Turn victim on side (supporting head and neck), maintain airway and sweep away any vomitus. Hold diver loosely to prevent self-injury and do not forcefully insert an airway or tongue blade. Resume oxygen administration when convulsions cease.
6. Protect the victim from excessive heat, cold, wetness, or noxious fumes.
7. For conscious victims only—Give non-alcoholic liquids orally such as water or fruit juices.
8. Transport the diver to the nearest emergency room to be evaluated and stabilized in preparation for transport to a recompression chamber.
9. Call DAN at (919) 684-8111. State that you have an emergency, and ask for the person on call. (If necessary, you can call collect in an emergency.)
10. If air evacuation will be used, it is critical that the victim not be further injured by exposure to decreased barometric pressure at altitude. Flight crews must maintain cabin pressure at sea level or fly at the lowest safe altitude in unpressurized aircraft.
11. Contact hyperbaric trauma center or chamber before transporting the victim.
12. If available, send a copy of DAN's *Underwater Diving Accident and Oxygen First Aid Manual*, and record history (dive profile, diver's complaints, medical history, and first aid) with the victim.
13. Send all diving equipment with the victim for examination. If that's not possible, arrange for local examination and gas analysis.

Bibliography

Bennett, P. B. & Elliot, D.H. (eds.) *The Physiology and Medicine of Diving,* Fourth Edition. London: Bailliere Tindall Limited, 1993.

Bookspan, J. "Decompression Theory in Plain English." *Sources: The Journal of Underwater Education.* National Association of Underwater Instructors: Montclair, CA, March/April 1990.

Bornmann, R.C. "History of Decompression Theory." *Proceedings of the 17th Undersea Medical Society Workshop—Decompression Theory.* Bethesda, MD: UHMS Publication Number 29WS (DT) 6-25-80, September 1978.

Boycott, A.E., G.C.C. Damant, and J.S. Haldane. "The Prevention of Compressed-Air Sickness," *Journal of Hygiene.* London, 1908.

Brylske, A.F. *The PADI Divemaster Manual.* Santa Ana, CA: Professional Association of Diving Instructors, 1985.

Coley, R. and G. Lewbel. *Computer-Assisted Multi-Level Diving Workbook.* Carlsbad, CA: Sea Quest, Inc., 1988.

des Granges, M. "Standards Air Decompression Tables," *U.S. Navy Experimental Diving Unit Report 5-57.* Washington, D.C., 1956.

Divers Alert Network. *1992 Report on Diving Accidents and Fatalities.* Durham, NC: Duke University, 1994.

Divers Alert Network. *DAN Underwater Diving Accident Manual.* Durham, NC: Duke University, 1985.

Hamilton, R.W., R.E. Rogers, M.R. Powell, and R.D. Vann. *The DSAT Recreational Dive Planner: Development and Validation of No-Stop Decompression Procedures for Recreational Diving.* Santa Ana, CA: Diving Science and Technology Corporation, 1994.

Huggins, K.E. "Ultrasound Doppler Study of Multilevel Diving Profiles," ORCA Industries publication, 1983.

Hunt, J. "Straightening out the Bends." *aquaCorps Journal*, No. 5, January 1993.

Laboda, A. "The Psychology of Decompression Sickness." *Dive Training*, April 1994.

Lang, M.A., and R.W. Hamilton (eds.). *American Academy of Underwater Scientists Dive Computer Workshop Proceeding.* Costa Mesa, CA: University of Southern California, Sea Grant Publication, (USCSG-TR-01-89), 1989.

Lang, M.A., and R.D. Vann (eds.). Proceedings of the American Academy of Underwater Sciences Workshop on Repetitive Diving Workshop, Duke University Medical Center, March 18019, 1991. *American Academy of Underwater Sciences*, January 1992.

Lanphier, E.H. "Sixty Feet Per Minute. Why?" *Sources: The Journal of Underwater Education.* Montclair, CA: National Association of Underwater Instructors, March/April 1990.

Lewis, J.E., and K.W. Shreeves. *Decompression Theory, Dive Tables and Dive Computers.* Santa Ana, CA: Professional Association of Diving Instructors, 1990.

Lippman, J. *Deeper into Diving.* Victoria, Australia: J.L. Publications, 1990.

Loyst, K., K. Huggins, and M. Steidley. *Dive Computers: A Consumer's Guide to History, Theory and Performance.* San Diego, CA: Watersports Publishing, Inc., 1991.

McMahon, B. "Homo Aquaticus and the Eight-Liter Lung." *Outside*, March 1994.

Miller, J.W., and I.G. Koblick. *Living and Working in the Sea.* New York: Van Nostrand Reinhold Company, 1984.

Nashimoto, I., and E.H. Lanphier. "What is Bends?" *Proceedings of the 43rd Undersea and Hyperbaric Medical Society Workshop.* Bethesda, MD: UHMS Publication Number 80 (Bends), May 1991.

National Association of Underwater Instructors. *Advanced Diving Techniques and Technology.* Montclair, CA: NAUI, 1989.

Nishi, R.Y. "Tiny Bubbles: A Primer on Doppler Ultrasonic Bubble Detection." *aquaCorps Journal,* No. 5, January 1993.

Pilmanis, A.A. "Intravenous Gas Emboli in Man after Compressed Air Ocean Diving," *Office of Naval Research Contract Report* (N00014-67-A-0269-0026), Washington, D.C., 1976.

Powell, M. "Unraveling the Mystery of Decompression Sickness," *The Undersea Journal*. Santa Ana, CA: Professional Association of Diving Instructors, fourth quarter, 1987.

Rogers, R.E. "The Dive Tables: A Different View," *The Undersea Journal*. Santa Ana, CA: Professional Association of Diving Instructors, first quarter, 1984.

Shreeves, Karl (ed.). *The Encyclopedia of Recreational Diving*. Santa Ana, CA: Professional Association of Diving Instructors, 1988.

Spencer, M.P. "Decompression Limits for Compressed Air Determined by Ultrasonically Detected Blood Bubbles," *Journal of Applied Physiology*. 40 (1976):229-35.

Strauss, R. *Diving Medicine*. New York: Grunet & Stratton, 1976.

Vallintine, R. *Divers and Diving*. Dorset, UK: Blandfort Press, 1981.

Westerfield, R.D. "New Navy Decompression Tables." *Alert Diver*. Durham, NC: Divers Alert Network, March/April 1994.

Wienke, B.R. "Bubble Quest: Developing Dive Tables and Computers is Still Not an Exact Science." *Alert Diver*. Durham, NC: Divers Alert Network, March/April 1994.

Wienke, B.R. "Safety Stops and Slow Ascent Rates." *Sources: The Journal of Underwater Education*. Montclair, CA: National Association of Underwater Instructors, March/April 1990.

Wilmshurst, P. "Cardiac Shunts and DCS." *Diver Magazine*. London: Eaton Publishing, February 1990.

Yount, D.E. "Bubble Mechanics: Implications for Safe Ascent." *Sources: The Journal of Underwater Education*. Montclair, CA: National Association of Underwater Instructors, March/April 1990.

Index

Actual bottom time (ABT) *59-60*

Adjusted maximum dive time (AMDT) *60-62*

Adjusted no-decompression limit (ANDL) *65*

Age, effect on DCS risk *14*

Altitude diving *70, 76, 104*

Anti-smooth muscle activating factor *11*

Anxiety, effect on DCS risk *15*

Arterial gas embolism (AGE) *25, 26, 106, 109*

Ascent rate *85, 88-91*

Behavior, effect on DCS risk *18*

Behnke, Albert *42-43*

Bends, origin of term *20*

Bert, Paul *30-31*

Blood chemistry *11-12*

Bottleneck effect *7, 22*

Bounce dives *23, 96*

Boyle, Robert *28*

Bubble formation *5-13, 16, 17, 32, 42-43*

Bubbles, asymptomatic *7*
  Extravascular *9*
  Silent *8, 42, 89, 92*
  Subclinical *7*

Buhlmann, Albert *76, 81*

Buoyancy control *93-95*

Caisson disease *30*

Caissons *20, 30*

Campbell, S.D. *43*

Carbon dioxide, effect on DCS risk *16*

Catalina Marine Science Center, study of safety stops *92*

Cerebral DCS *23*

Chysssanthou *11*

Cold, effect on DCS risk *17*

Coma position *106-107*

Compartment *34, 79-81*

Crilley, Frank *37*

Cyberdriver *75-76*

Dacor Corp. *76*

Damant, G.C.C. *36*

Datamaster II *76*

Data Scan *2 76*

DCIEM Tables *49, 65, **66-67**, 68-70*

DDC computer *76*

Decobrain computers *76*

Decompression diving *68-69, 83, 86, 88-89*

Decompression illness *25-26*

Decompression models *10, 13, 17*

Decompression stop *40, 91*

Decomputer *74*

Deep diving, efffect on DCS risk *18*

Deep pain *9*

Defence and Civil Institute of Environmental Medicine (DCIEM) *48, 65, 73, 75*

Deserved hit *112*

Dehydration *12, 14*

Denial of DCS *19*

Des Granges, M. *39*

Diffusion *12*

Disordered decompression sickness *13*

Dissolved phase dynamics *50*

Dive computers *54, 71-87, 90*
  Components *77-79*
  History *72-77*
  Safe use guidelines *83-87*
  Schematic **78**

Dive profile *58*

Dive states *51*

Divers Alert Network (DAN) *9-10, 22, 70, 87, 96, 100, 108*

Divetronic Corp. *76*

Diving Science and Technology Corp. (DSAT) *46-47, 62, 81*

Doppler Bubble Detector **10, 43***, 43-45, 48-49, 89*

Driving to altitude *104*

Drugs and alcohol, effect on DCS risk *15*

Drug therapy *109*

Dwyer, J.V. *39*

Edema *12*

Edge computer *76,* **76**

E-E model *47, 79-81*

Effective bottom time (EBT) *70*

Effervescence *2*

E-L model *47*

Experimental Diving Unit *37, 50, 72, 74*

Exponential relationship *34*

Farallon Industries *74*

Feet-up, head-low position *106*

First aid *105-115*

Pressure transducer *74*
Predisposition factors *13-18*
Probabilistic model *51*
Professional Association of Diving Instructors (PADI) *46, 81*
Psychology *112-114*
Pulmonary DCS *22*
Recompression *11 108-109, 112*
Recreational Dive Planner *47, 62, **63-64**, 65, 68-69, 81*
Repetitive dive depth *59*
Repetitive diving *10, 23, 36, 46, 65, 69-70, 79, 86, 96*
Repetitive factor (RF) *69*
Repetitive group *40, 53-54, 58, 65, 68*
Residual nitrogen time *51, 59, 60, 62, 65*
Risk of DCS *13-18, 70, 96-97*
Reverse profiles *96*
Rogers, Raymond *45-47, 69*
Royal Navy *32, 36, 89*
Safety stop *44, 85-86, 91-95*
    Guidelines *93-95*
Saturation *3*
Sawtooth profiles *96*
Scubapro Corp. *72*
Seeds, gas *6-**8**, 17, 50*
Serial model *48*
Shilling, Charles *37-38*
Shunting *23*
Siebe Gorman & Company *36*
Skin bends *22*
Sludging *12, 102*
Smooth muscle activating factor *11*
Snorkeling and DCS *97-98*
Solubility of gases *4*
SOS Diving Equipment Company *72*
SOS Meter *72-73, **73***
Spencer, Merrill *43*
Spinal DCS *22*
Staggers *23*
Stasis *14*
Stillson, George *36-37*
Strauss, Michael *13*
Stubbs, R.A. *48, 65, 73*
Supersaturation
Surface decompression *38*
Surface interval *62, 68-69*
Surfacing ratio *33, 36, 38, 40-41*
Susceptibility factors *13-18*

Symptoms of DCS *19, 21-23, 106*
Table-based computer *75, 79*
Temperature, effect on gas absorption *3-5*
Texas Research Associates *73*
Thalmann, Ed *41, 47, 50*
Third spacing *12*
Tiny bubble model *50*
Tissue *34, 73-74*
Total bottom time (TBT) *59-60, 62, 65*
TRACOR Electronic Analog Computer *74*
Treatment of DCS *105-115*
    Oxygen *107-108*
    Positioning *106-107*
Treatment tables *109-110*
Trendelenburg position *106*
Triger *29*
Type I *21*
Type II *21*
Undersea and Hyperbaric Medical Society (UHMS) *99-101*
Undeserved hit *112*
U.S. Divers Company *76*
U.S. Navy Tables *27, 36-42, 50-51, 55-60, **56-57**, 74, 76, 79, 89, 99*
Van der Aue, O.E. *38*
Walkie, USS *37*
Wattelle *29*
Weathersby, Paul *50-51*
Wienke, Bruce *50, 81*
Workman, Robert *39-40*
XDC Digital Decompression Computers *75*
Yarbrough, O.D. *38*
Yount, David *50*